INORGANIC PREPARATIONS

A Laboratory Manual

By

HAROLD FREDERIC WALTON

Assistant Professor of Chemistry
University of Colorado

PRENTICE-HALL, INC.
Englewood Cliffs, N. J.

PRENTICE-HALL CHEMISTRY SERIES

WENDELL M. LATIMER, PH.D., *Editor*

First Printing........December, 1948
Second Printing..........May, 1950
Third Printing.......December, 1953
Fourth Printing.....November, 1955
Fifth Printing.......September, 1957
Sixth Printing..........March, 1959
Seventh Printing......January, 1961
Eighth Printing..........June, 1962
Ninth Printing........March, 1965

PRINTED IN THE UNITED STATES OF AMERICA

46670-C

Preface

This manual of inorganic preparations grew out of a one-quarter lecture course in descriptive inorganic chemistry which the author gave for a number of years at Northwestern University. Laboratory work (three hours a week) was optional. The course, intended primarily for senior and junior undergraduates, was designed to give a more detailed account of inorganic chemistry than that of the freshman year and to prepare the student for an advanced graduate course in structural inorganic chemistry and valence theory. Since many students who had not had a descriptive survey came to Northwestern to do graduate work, these graduate students also took this course and often elected to do the laboratory work.

The problem was, therefore, to work out a number of experiments in preparative inorganic chemistry which would be suitable both for undergraduate students above the freshman year and for first-year graduate students, and which could be correlated with the lecture course. To achieve this end, a number of experiments were taken from older manuals, in particular that of H. and W. Biltz, and modified to meet the needs of the course. Other experiments were adapted for instructional purposes from the original literature, especially from *Inorganic Syntheses*, and a few are original with the writer.

The introductory chapters of this book present some of the general principles and theories which help to interpret the experiments, for example valence theory, covalence and the periodic table, coordination, oxidation and reduction, and phase equilibria. The treatment given here is, of course, brief and should be supplemented by lectures and by further reading. It is assumed that the student is already familiar with the fundamentals of atomic structure, the periodic system, and the principles of chemical equilibrium; that is, that he has had a year course in general chemistry and qualitative analysis and an introduction to quantitative analysis.

The writer would like to thank the many students at Northwestern University who helped to work out the experiments, and in particular Miss Isabelle Ryden. He also thanks his colleagues who have given their help and encouragement, particularly Professors R. K. Summerbell, A. A. Frost, and F. Basolo, of Northwestern University, and Professor H. B. Van Valkenburgh of the University of Colorado.

The diagrams in the text were drawn by Mr. William Parker of the University of Colorado.

HAROLD F. WALTON

Boulder, Colorado

Contents

[See page vii for complete list of preparations by type.]

List of Preparations

A. COMPOUNDS

B. REACTIONS

OXIDATIONS

REDUCTIONS

ELECTROLYTIC PREPARATIONS

CHAPTER I

Introduction:
A Course in Inorganic Preparations

The aims of a course in inorganic preparations are, first, to learn the common techniques and reactions of preparative inorganic chemistry, and second, to become acquainted with the appearance and properties of typical inorganic substances. This manual has been written with these aims in mind. Fifty-two experiments are described, in which samples of some 70 substances are prepared. The experiments have been chosen to illustrate a variety of reactions, techniques, and substances.

This text differs from such works as *Inorganic Syntheses* and Vanino's *Handbuch der präparativen Chemie* (see the bibliography at the end of this chapter) in that its purpose is educational rather than strictly practical. The preparations in this manual are not chosen primarily because they give products that are useful in the laboratory, though some are useful, such as silver nitrate from silver residues in Experiment 41. Nor are the directions written for large quantities of material, though the preparations can usually be performed with larger quantities if desired. Some of the preparations in this manual are made on the gram scale or smaller, such as anhydrous ferric and ferrous chlorides in Experiment 21, but the usual scale is 10 to 50 grams. Some preparations are included for the techniques they embody, such as the furnace reduction in Experiment 43 or the electrolytic preparations; some are included to illustrate certain types of reaction or because the properties of the products illustrate important chemical generalizations. as in Experiments 10, 21, and 36; other preparations

1

are included because of the important industrial applications of the products, as in Experiments 22 and 29. The classification of these experiments offered a problem. It was decided to group them, in part, according to the type of compound produced and, in part, according to the type of reaction illustrated in the preparation.

Most of the experiments can be performed by a class of 10 or 20 in a laboratory with average facilities, and they need, on the average, about 3 hours' working time each. Very long preparations and preparations involving complicated equipment or expensive chemicals have been avoided. It may be desirable for a few students to perform such preparations, but they can always refer for details to the original literature.

In nearly every experiment in this manual, tests are made on the product to study its properties, and in several instances directions are given for analyzing the product quantitatively to determine its purity. Volumetric methods of assaying are given, since they are quicker than gravimetric methods and often just as accurate.

A set of questions is appended to each experiment. Some of these questions will be answered by the experiment itself; that is, they concern reactions or phenomena that occur in the experiment but are not described explicitly in the directions. Many of the questions involve periodic system relationships, and it is to help answer such questions that Chapters IV and V of the preliminary text are included. There is more system, logic, and correlation to inorganic chemistry than is generally appreciated, and any course in descriptive inorganic chemistry, whether a laboratory course or not, should emphasize this system. It is also important to understand the physical principles used in separating a pure product or in guiding a reaction to obtain the desired substance; for this reason Chapters III, VI and VII are included, and a number of the questions on the various experiments concern these principles. Other questions relate to industrial applications.

The student should keep his laboratory notebook after the manner of a research notebook. It should be written up as the work proceeds. The student is not asked to copy the directions from this manual nor to give a finished literary account; the entries may be brief and telegraphic in style, but they should be so clear and complete that another person can look at the notebook and find out exactly what the student has done. All *quantities of materials* taken should be noted, and, where significant, should be expressed in moles as well as grams. All relevant *temperatures, flow rates, reaction times*, and so on, should be noted, and the *yield of product* should be expressed in grams and moles and as a percentage of the maximum theoretical yield unless the instructions say otherwise. The *percentage purity* should also be clearly stated where this has been determined. *Equations* for all reactions should be given in the account. (In the instructions in this manual, the equations are generally omitted and are left for the student to supply.) In particular, the notebook report should mention any colorations, precipitates, or other effects that are not described in the manual. The directions in the manual are complete enough that, with good technique, a good yield of product will be obtained, but they do not describe everything that is going to happen.

After the various tests have been made, the entire product, if a solid or liquid, should be submitted to the instructor in a labeled specimen bottle or suitable container.

Sufficient experiments are included for a whole year's course and more. The selection of experiments for a one-quarter course will depend on the students taking the course and on the wishes of the instructor, but the writer suggests the following selection for a class of senior undergraduates.

1. Purification of Sodium Chloride.

4. Double Salts. These illustrate crystallization techniques.

9. Potassium Ferric Oxalate. This experiment introduces complex ions and compares the stability of different complex ions.

40. Cuprous Chloride. This introduces washing with alcohol and ether and the handling of a product that is sensitive to the air.

45. Chromous Acetate. This illustrates variable valence in the transition elements and is a severe test of technique.

46. Ferric and Ferrous Chloride.

16. Aluminum Bromide. These show the effect of ionic charge on valence type and the differences between ionic and covalent compounds.

42. Barium Chloride. Illustrates the use of the Fletcher furnace. To get a clean product and good yield requires a little skill.

22. Silica Gel. This experiment shows that not all solids are crystalline and that "sodium silicate" is not a single chemical individual. The calculation of the theoretical yield is interesting.

38. Potassium Permanganate. An example of alkaline oxidation and a test of clean technique.

39. Potassium Iodate. Shows that chlorine does not always displace iodine. (Some of the students may do Experiment 46 instead.)

25. Nitrogen dioxide. Illustrates the handling and condensation of a gas.

BOOKS FOR REFERENCE AND STUDY

In any laboratory work in preparative chemistry, a handbook of data, such as Lange's *Handbook of Chemistry*, 6th ed. (Handbook Publishers, 1946), should always be at hand for constant reference. Knowledge of solubilities, melting and boiling points, vapor pressures, and so on is essential in planning a preparation, and these data can be found in the *Handbook*. Where necessary, the *Handbook* should be supplemented by *International Critical Tables* (New York: McGraw-Hill, 1926–1930; 7 volumes). Many of the data in International Critical Tables are given in the form of fundamental thermodynamic constants, and the student should know, for instance, how to calculate the dissociation pressure of copper sulfate pentahydrate at 50° from a free energy equation.

In addition, the following books should be available for reference or study:

FOR PREPARATIVE INORGANIC CHEMISTRY

Inorganic Syntheses: Vol. I (1939), edited by H. S. Booth; Vol. II (1946), edited by W. C. Fernelius. New York: McGraw-Hill.

Vanino, L.: *Handbuch der präparativen Chemie. Band I: Anorganische Chemie.* Reprinted by Edwards Brothers, Ann Arbor, Michigan.

Blanchard, A. A., J. W. Phelan, and A. R. Davis: *Synthetic Inorganic Chemistry,* 5th ed. New York: Wiley, 1936.

FOR VALENCE THEORY AND STRUCTURAL CHEMISTRY

Sidgwick, N. V., *The Electronic Theory of Valency.* Oxford University Press, 1929.

———, *The Covalent Link in Chemistry.* Ithaca: Cornell University Press, 1933.

Pauling, L., *The Nature of the Chemical Bond,* 2d ed. Ithaca: Cornell University Press, 1940.

Palmer, W. G., *Valency, Classical and Modern.* Cambridge University Press, 1944.

Wells, A. F., *Structural Inorganic Chemistry.* Oxford University Press, 1945.

FOR DESCRIPTIVE INORGANIC CHEMISTRY, WITH EMPHASIS ON CHEMICAL PRINCIPLES

Partington, J. R., *Inorganic Chemistry,* 5th ed. London: Macmillan, 1939.

Latimer, W. M., and J. H. Hildebrand, *Reference Book of Inorganic Chemistry.* New York: Macmillan, 1940.

Yost, D. M., and H. Russell, *Systematic Inorganic Chemistry.* New York: Prentice-Hall, 1944.

CHAPTER II

Equipment

For a course in inorganic preparations, the equipment that every student should have in his desk is approximately the following:

Clamps, clamp holders, retort stand, retort rings, tripod

Wire gauze, pipe-clay triangles, Bunsen burner, a Meker or Fisher burner

Porcelain, iron, and nickel crucibles with covers

An iron dish about 12 cm in diameter and 1.5 cm deep

Crucible tongs

Beakers, assorted sizes

Erlenmeyer flasks, 250 ml and 500 ml

Florence flasks, 1000 ml; round-bottom flask, 500 ml

Distilling flask, 250 ml

Funnels, 60 deg, 70 mm diameter, and 11-cm filter paper

Separatory funnel, 60 ml

Büchner funnels, to take 90-mm and 40-mm filter paper; filter papers to fit

Büchner flask, 500 ml

Desiccator

Thermometer, $-10°$ to $250°C$

Evaporating dishes, assorted sizes, including one of diameter 16 cm

Pestle and mortar (10 cm diameter)

Test tubes, Pyrex, 25×200 mm and smaller; test-tube rack

Burette, 50 ml; pipette, 10 ml; volumetric flask, 100 ml; weighing bottle

Graduated cylinders, 10 ml and 100 ml

Watch glasses, assorted sizes

Spatulas, steel and glass

6 sample bottles, wide mouth, screw cap, 2 oz (60 ml)

Rubber tubing (including pressure tubing), rubber and cork stoppers

Glass tubing and rod; test-tube brushes, cloth, matches, labels

The equipment that should be provided for common use includes the following:

Balances; torsion balance sensitive to 0.5 gram, also an analytical balance sensitive to 1 mg

Steam baths; ovens giving temperatures up to 200°

Aspirator pumps

Large ($2\frac{1}{2}$-liter) glass bottles, large evaporating dishes, flasks

Gas washing bottles (preferably of the spiral type), absorption tubes and towers, sintered glass filters (of Büchner and other forms), combustion tubes of high-melting Pyrex and sillimanite.

Electrical equipment for electrolysis; ammeters, voltmeters, rheostats, porous cups (see electrolytic preparations)

Equipment with interchangeable ground-glass joints, for distillations and similar operations

Centrifuge, clinical or desk-top type, to hold 12-ml tubes (convenient but not necessary)

Large Meker burners and ring burners. For heating iron crucibles and dishes in the air to as high a temperature as possible, as in Experiment 38, it is convenient to have a number of pieces of asbestos board with circular holes cut so the dish will rest as deeply in the hole as possible without slipping through.

Large mortars and pestles. If much work with ores is to be undertaken and if the ores cannot be obtained ready-ground, a laboratory-scale rock crusher either power-driven or hand-operated, should be made available. A convenient type of crusher, which is also useful for crushing glasses such as the boron trioxide obtained in Experiment 15, consists simply of a large hemisphere of iron, about 9 in. across, with a handle attached, which can be rotated in an iron mortar which it fits closely. A peg in the base of the mortar engages with a socket in the bottom of the iron hemisphere.

A small ball mill of steel or stoneware is convenient for fine pulverizing of mineral samples or for producing very intimate mixing of solid powders, as in Experiments 42 and 43.

Furnaces. Two types of furnace are needed: a crucible furnace and a combustion-tube furnace. A muffle furnace is also useful but is not necessary for the experiments in this book. The most generally useful type of crucible furnace and also the cheapest, is the Fletcher gas furnace (Fig. 1). This is simply a cylindrical block of fire clay with a cavity in it large enough to take a 200-ml Hessian fire-clay crucible, an opening on the side at the bottom of this cavity to admit a gas flame, and an outlet at the top. The burner is of the horizontal Meker type, fed by gas and compressed air, which is pointed against the bottom opening. In starting a cold Fletcher furnace, the gas should not be turned full on at first, nor should the proportion of air be as large as will be admitted later; otherwise the flame is likely to go out. When the inside of the furnace becomes red hot, the gas and air supplies can be increased. The air supply should be great enough that no flame is seen issuing from the flue at the top of the furnace. When it is time to turn the furnace off, first the burner should be removed from the furnace; then the gas should be turned off, then the air. If the burner is left against the furnace opening after it is turned out, the heat of the furnace will melt the brass grid of the burner.

The Fletcher furnace should not be stood directly on the laboratory bench but should be supported on bricks. It gets very hot; a temperature of 1200°C is easily reached inside the furnace. A disadvantage is that the heat is not

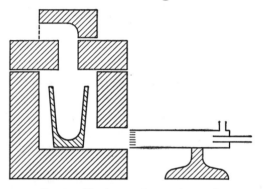

Fig. 1. Fletcher gas furnace (section).

uniform, being most intense where the gas flame hits the side of the crucible. If the charge in the furnace contains alkaline material, there is danger of perforating the crucible at this point (in Experiment 41, for example). In such a case the full heat of the flame should not be used. It is always a sensible precaution to spread a little sand on the bottom of the furnace chamber before putting the crucible in. Then if the crucible does crack or perforate, the damage to the furnace will not be so great.

Electric crucible furnaces are also obtainable. They have the advantages of a uniform and easily controlled temperature, and of easy exclusion of oxygen from the crucible chamber. However, they do not produce as high a temperature as the gas furnace, 1000°C being the usual maximum. The crucibles usually used in these furnaces are the Hessian fire-clay type, which are very cheap, so that if they have to be broken open to remove the contents there is no great loss.

Combustion-tube furnaces. Electrically heated combustion-tube furnaces are now used almost exclusively on account of the uniform and reproducible heating they give. Again, the highest temperature usually obtainable is 1100°. A gas-fired furnace gives a somewhat higher temperature and heats up more quickly.

Some electric tube furnaces incorporate a pyrometer, which is not required in any of the experiments described in this manual, though Experiments 13 and 14 can be run by using an electric tube furnace at controlled temperature instead of an oil bath if so desired. A pyrometer may easily be improvised with iron and constantan wires twisted together and spot-welded to provide the junctions. The "hot" junction is placed against the outside of the combustion tube in the center of the heated portion and bound in position by asbestos tape, which also serves as insulation. The "cold" junction is kept in ice and water, and the electromotive force is measured with a millivoltmeter. With the cold junction at 0°C and the hot junction at 200°C, the electromotive force of the iron-constantan couple is given in tables as 10.77 millivolts. For accurate work the couple used should be calibrated; and to assure uniform temperature distribution and electrical shielding, the combustion-tube and thermocouple wires should be encased in a tubular metal shield that fits inside the furnace and is grounded.

CHAPTER III

Crystallization, Filtration, Washing and Drying

CRYSTALLIZATION

Most inorganic compounds are solids that are soluble in water. Crystallization from an aqueous solution is the usual way to isolate and purify such compounds. The solution is evaporated by boiling, or by heating in an open dish so that the solvent evaporates without boiling, until crystals begin to appear. It is then allowed to cool; and since the solubility of most substances decreases as the temperature falls, more crystals separate on cooling. Slow cooling gives larger and usually purer crystals than does rapid cooling. The yield to be expected can be found from solubility tables.

The impurities in the solution should remain behind in the mother liquor; therefore it is important to leave enough mother liquor to hold the impurities and not to carry the evaporation so far that the impurities crystallize out along with the desired product. In evaporating in a dish, the solution must be kept stirred to avoid the formation of crusts of crystals around the sides of the dish, since these always retain some of the mother liquor, which evaporates completely to dryness and deposits all the impurities.

If the salt is not much less soluble in the cold than in the hot, as is true of sodium chloride (whose solubility in 100 grams of water is 35.7 grams at 0°, 39.8 grams at 100°), only a small proportion will crystallize out on cooling, and the rest will stay in solution. In such a case the solution can simply be evaporated or boiled down until enough of the salt has separated out.   During this evaporation one must be careful to avoid the formation of crusts, for the reason given in the last paragraph.   In the laboratory, a better way than evaporation is often to add a substance having an ion in common with the salt to be precipitated, which will decrease the solubility of the latter in accordance with the solubility-product principle.   Thus sodium chloride can be precipitated from its saturated solution by passing in hydrogen chloride gas, and the crystals produced are very pure (Experiment 1).   Another example of precipitating a salt from solution by the common-ion effect is given in Experiment 10.

A dissolved substance can also be made to crystallize by adding a liquid which will mix with water but which is a poor solvent for the substance to be crystallized.   Thus tetrammine cupric sulfate is precipitated from solution in Experiment 5 by adding alcohol.   Evaporation could not be used to crystallize this salt, since ammonia would be lost on boiling and the salt would decompose.   Another instance of the addition of a second solvent to bring about crystallization is in Experiment 26, in which chromium trioxide is made to crystallize by adding excess of sulfuric acid.   Here the desired product is so very soluble in water that it could not be crystallized in pure form by evaporation.

Phase diagrams.   Crystallization from a solution is a selective process.   It can be used to purify a desired product from unwanted impurities and also to separate the components of fairly complicated mixtures.   A very careful control over temperature and composition of the solution is needed to obtain pure products, and an exact knowledge of solubility relations is required.   Such knowledge is summarized in *phase diagrams*, which are as useful and necessary in selective crystallizations as are road maps to the motorist.   For a complete discussion of phase diagrams the reader is referred to textbooks of physical chemistry or to treatises on the phase rule.[1] The following treatment is introductory only.

The graph in Fig. 2 is the familiar solubility curve of potassium chloride, showing the solubility of the salt at different temperatures. This is a phase diagram, though a simple one, since the only two phases we are considering are solid potassium chloride and its aqueous solution. (One phase is distinguished from another phase by a sharp boundary at which the physical or chemical properties

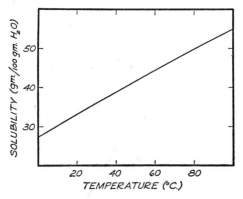

Fig. 2. Solubility of potassium chloride.

change abruptly. Each phase is uniform and homogeneous within itself if everything is at equilibrium.) The composition of the saturated aqueous solution depends on pressure as well as temperature, but the influence of pressure is very small and may be neglected. A single line is then sufficient to relate the two variables, temperature and solubility.

Figure 3 is the solubility curve for sodium chloride in water. It will be seen that temperature has much less effect on the solubility of sodium chloride than on that of potassium chloride, and we can see already that it should be possible to separate a mixture of these two salts by evaporating and cooling. If conditions are favorable, potassium

[1] See, for example, A. Findlay and A. N. Campbell, *The Phase Rule and Its Applications*, 8th ed. New York: Longmans, 1938.

chloride alone, free from sodium chloride, will separate as the mixture is cooled, owing to its steeper solubility curve; but these diagrams are for the pure salts separately and give no quantitative information on how mixtures of the two salts will behave.

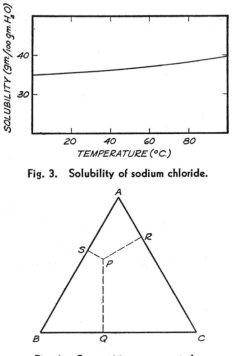

Fig. 3.   Solubility of sodium chloride.

Fig. 4.   Compositions represented on a triangular diagram.

Where we have two salts dissolved in the same solvent, we can no longer represent the solution composition by one coordinate in a graph as we did above, since the percentage of salt A and the percentage of salt B can be varied quite independently of one another.   However, if the percentages of A and B have been chosen, we can no longer choose the percentage of solvent to be anything we like; it is fixed. Geometrically, the composition of a mixture of three substances (or components) can be expressed by a point within an equilateral triangle. In Fig. 4 the point P represents a mixture in which the amounts of the components A, B, and C are in proportion to the lengths of the lines PQ, PR, and PS, drawn from P at right angles to the sides of the triangle. The sum of these three lengths is constant wherever we put P and is equal to the length of the perpendicular from one of the corners to the opposite side. The corner A of the triangle represents pure A, since if we move P to A, the lengths PR and PS become zero.

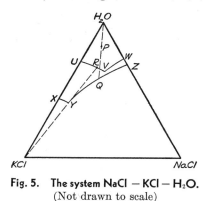

Fig. 5. The system NaCl — KCl — H$_2$O.
(Not drawn to scale)

In Fig. 5 this method of representing compositions is used to show the solubilities of NaCl and KCl in solutions containing both of the salts. The line UVW represents the solubilities at 20°, XYZ the solubilities at 100°. (Note that it is necessary to draw one line for each temperature. These are contour lines for the three-dimensional surface that we should get if we erected a temperature axis at right angles to the plane of the triangle and then plotted the complete solubility graph.) The segments UV and XY represent the compositions of saturated solutions in equilibrium with solid KCl; the segments VW and YZ represent solutions in equilibrium with solid NaCl.

Let us use this diagram to see what would happen if we evaporated a solution of composition represented by the point P at a temperature of 100°. As water is removed, the composition moves along the line PQ; at Q, crystals of

NaCl are deposited, the solution becomes poorer in NaCl and relatively richer in KCl, and the point representing the composition moves along the line QY. At the point Y, both NaCl and KCl would crystallize simultaneously. However, if the solution is now cooled to 20° at this stage, pure KCl separates, the composition of the solution meanwhile moving along the line YR. At equilibrium at 20°, we have a saturated solution of composition R, in equilibrium with pure solid KCl.

By proper manipulation of this process, therefore, we can obtain considerable amounts of pure potassium chloride from a solution containing both sodium and potassium chlorides. This technique is actually used to recover potassium chloride from the brine of Searles Lake, in California, which is a partially dried-up lake saturated with sodium chloride. Since the brine contains carbonate, sulfate, and borate ions as well as Na^+, K^+, and Cl^-, the solubility relations are more complex, but the principle is the same as that just described.[2]   One may ask, Why does *pure* potassium chloride separate out on cooling? Why should not a little sodium chloride separate out as well, seeing that its solubility decreases somewhat as the temperature drops? The reason, essentially, is that as the potassium chloride separates, the chloride ion concentration gets less, and by the common-ion effect this *increases* the solubility of sodium chloride, more than offsetting the effect of the temperature drop.

An example of a very difficult crystallization, where compositions and temperatures must be watched very closely to get the desired product, is the production of sodium chromate. Sodium chromate, Na_2CrO_4, is extremely soluble and crystallizes only in a limited concentration range where a considerable excess of sodium hydroxide is present. If the solution is not strongly basic, other salts such as $Na_2Cr_2O_7$ or $Na_2Cr_3O_{10}$ may crystallize.[3]

---

[2] G. R. Robertson, *Ind. Eng. Chem.*, **21** (1929), 520, and **34** (1942), 133.
[3] F. A. H. Schreinemakers, *Z. Phys. Chem.*, **55** (1906), 71.

It must be emphasized that separation of complex mixtures by crystallization is far easier on the industrial scale than in the laboratory. In large plants it is easier to control the temperature and concentration, and to separate crystals and mother liquor quickly and efficiently.

Experiment 2 in this manual illustrates the use of phase diagrams in choosing the right compositions and temperatures for the preparation of double salts.

Solid solutions. In the preceding discussion we have assumed that the salts that separate from mixed solutions are pure. If we happen to have just the right composition and temperature to be at the intersection of two solubility curves, as at points V and Y in Fig. 5, two salts will crystallize side by side, but otherwise only one salt crystallizes at a time; no solid solutions are formed. Usually this is the case. Each salt has its own crystal lattice, and foreign ions having different charges or sizes are not incorporated into the lattice. Even ions as similar as Na^+ and K^+ do not usually enter into each other's crystal lattice. NaCl does not form mixed crystals with KCl, because the radii of the sodium and potassium ions are too dissimilar (0.98 Å and 1.33 Å, respectively). But if the ions are near enough in size (usually within 10 per cent of one another) and have similar polarizabilities and the same charge, mixed crystal lattices are possible in which a certain proportion of one ion is replaced by another. Thus $MnSO_4 \cdot 7H_2O$ and $FeSO_4 \cdot 7H_2O$ form such "solid solutions" or "mixed crystals," since both salts form monoclinic crystals and the ionic radii (Mn^{++} 0.91 Å, Fe^{++} 0.83Å) are nearly the same. Another pair of salts that form a range of solid solutions are KCl and KBr (radii, Cl^- 1.81 Å, Br^- 1.96 Å); sulfates and selenates are yet another example. Where a pair of salts form solid solutions, it is very difficult to separate them by fractional crystallization, since the crystals of one salt are always contaminated by the other salt, the contamination being greater the closer the solubilities of the two salts. Sometimes, repeated recrystallizations are necessary to get a satisfactory separation. This is true to an extreme degree in the rare-earth series, in which the ionic radii are close together, and a long and tedious series of recrystallizations is necessary to get a salt of even 90 to 95 per cent purity. Another fractional crystallization of practical interest is the separation of radium bromide from barium bromide. Here again, solid solutions are formed and many recrystallizations are necessary.

Where two salts that form solid solutions are to be separated, it is far better to use chemical methods of separation where possible. Suppose it were necessary to prepare pure $MnSO_4 \cdot 7H_2O$ from a quantity of the salt contaminated with ferrous sulfate. Rather than to attempt a direct recrystallization it would be better to dissolve the salt in water, oxidize the ferrous sulfate to ferric by means of chlorine water, neutralize carefully to pH 5 with ammonia to precipitate all the iron as hydrated ferric oxide, and then recrystallize the manganous sulfate. Other separation methods that can be used in such cases are the fractional distillation of volatile compounds and ion exchange; both of these methods have been used in separating the rare-earth elements.[4]

FILTERING AND WASHING

Filtering. In most laboratory preparations, crystals or precipitates are best collected on a Büchner funnel, using suction. If the precipitate is gelatinous, like silica gel in Experiment 22, it is best to filter in a large conical funnel under gravity and to use fluted filter paper. Alternatively, pour the solution into a canvas bag, fold over the end to close the bag, and press it between wooden boards in a hand-operated screw press to squeeze out the mother liquor.

Centrifuging is a very efficient way to separate a crystalline precipitate from its mother liquor. On the laboratory

[4] G. T. Morgan and H. W. Moss, *J. Chem. Soc.*, (1914,) 196; F. H. Spedding, A. F. Voigt, E. M. Gladrow, and N. R. Sleight, *J. Am. Chem. Soc.*, **69** (1947), 2777.

scale, the drained precipitate is placed in a basket of fine-mesh platinum or tantalum gauze that fits into the cup of a centrifuge; on spinning the centrifuge, the remaining mother liquor is thrown free of the crystals. This technique was used by T. W. Richards in preparing very pure salts for atomic-weight determinations. Centrifugal drying is much used in industry; the slurry of crystals and solution is poured into a gauze cylinder or bucket rotating at high speed. This gives the rapid and efficient filtration necessary in separating pure crystals from complex mixtures in solution, as in the treatment of Searles Lake brine (see above). A makeshift centrifugal drier for use in the laboratory with a few grams of material can be made by packing two balanced 12-ml centrifuge tubes half full of glass wool, tamping down to give a flat surface, and putting 2 to 3 ml of the crystal slurry in each and then centrifuging. This method is useful in Experiment 6, where the first product, potassium mercuriiodide, is very soluble and difficult to wash, and also in the second part of Experiment 4.

Washing. The secret of successful washing of a solid on a Büchner funnel is, first, never to let the mass on the filter dry out, and second, to use several small quantities of wash liquid rather than one large lot. If the precipitate is sucked too dry after filtration, the cake will crack and channels will develop; and when the wash liquid is poured on, it will all go down the cracks instead of permeating the entire mass. Therefore the best procedure is to turn off the suction while there is still a millimeter or so of water above the precipitate, and then the minute the water drains to the surface of the precipitate, to pour on the wash liquid and suck this through very slowly. Just as the level of liquid drops to the surface of the cake of precipitate, the second lot of wash liquid is poured on, and so on. When washing is completed (as judged by experience or by testing the wash liquid for impurities), the suction should be turned on full to suck as much liquid as possible from the cake.

Water is the usual wash liquid, but other liquids may be

used if the solid is soluble in water; for example, concentrated nitric acid is used to wash chromium trioxide in Experiment 26. Often a solid is washed first with water, then with another liquid to remove the water. If this second liquid is sufficiently volatile, it will evaporate and leave the precipitate dry without the precipitate having to be heated above room temperature. Acetone is a good liquid for this purpose, since it is completely miscible with water as well as being easily volatile. Another procedure is to wash the solid first with alcohol and then with ether. The alcohol washes the water out, and the ether washes out the alcohol and is very volatile, so that it evaporates as soon as the precipitate is spread out to dry. One cannot wash the precipitate directly with ether, since it will not mix with water to more than a very small extent.

It must be emphasized that the function of an alcohol or acetone wash is to remove *water* from the solid and not to remove adherent salts. Most salts are very poorly soluble in alcohol and acetone, and they must be washed out completely with water before the second solvent is added.

The economy of wash liquid obtained by using several small quantities of liquid instead of one large one is important where the wash liquid is costly, as in the case of ether, or where the precipitate is appreciably soluble. Speedy washing with a minimum amount of liquid is desirable if the moist or impure precipitate is easily oxidized by air. Thus quick and efficient washing is needed in the preparation of cuprous chloride (Experiment 40) and is absolutely essential in the preparation of chromous acetate (Experiment 45). In the latter experiment the precipitate of chromous acetate separates from a mother liquor that is rich in sodium acetate and zinc chloride, and these salts must all be washed out of the precipitate before the latter can be dried. At the same time the precipitate is appreciably soluble in water and is very easily oxidized. Hence ice water that has been freed from air is used for washing, and it is a good idea to keep the air out by covering the Büchner funnel loosely with a large cork carrying a tube through which carbon dioxide is passing.

DRYING

The temperature and other conditions under which a product should be dried vary widely. Cuprous chloride is dried with alcohol and ether at room temperature, sodium chloride can be dried completely in an oven at 110°, and magnesium chloride has to be heated gradually in presence of hydrogen chloride gas to 270°, whereas temperatures to 1000° are necessary to dry precipitated silica or alumina completely. Broadly, we can distinguish four kinds of bound water that have to be removed on drying: solution water, as in moist calcium chloride or in ordinary concentrated sulfuric acid; water of crystallization, as in the various hydrates of magnesium chloride; adsorbed water, held by capillary or surface forces, as in silica or alumina gel; and occluded water, which is held mechanically in cracks and cavities between crystals and is released when the crystals are ground up. The last two kinds of water usually give the most trouble when a very dry product is desired. T. W. Richards in his atomic-weight work made a practice of melting his salts wherever possible, as this was the best way to make sure that all occluded or adsorbed water was released. Richards also introduced a simple device for bottling dried salts without having them come into contact with the atmosphere.[5]

The evaporation of saturated solutions and the stability of salt hydrates can be treated by the phase rule. According to the rule,

No. of phases + No. of degrees of freedom
$$= \text{No. of components} + 2$$

Let us consider a system of two components, salt and water. (If the salt forms hydrates, the number of compo-

[5] T. W. Richards et al., Z. Anorg. Chem., **8** (1895), 267; J. Amer. Chem. Soc., **32** (1910), 4.

nents is not increased, since the hydrates are made up of salt and water only. The number of components is the minimum number of chemical individuals that must be brought together to make up the system.) If we have the saturated solution in equilibrium with solid salt and water vapor, the number of phases is three, and the system has

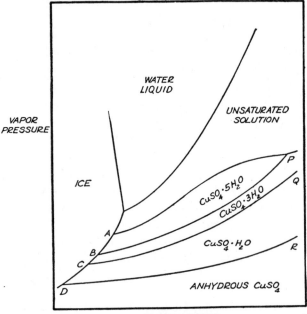

Fig. 6. The system CuSO₄ — H₂O.
(Not drawn to scale)

one degree of freedom. The same is true if we have a hydrate and the anhydrous salt, or two different hydrates, in equilibrium with each other and water vapor. For these systems we can choose the temperature if we wish, or we can choose the water vapor pressure; but having chosen one, we have determined the second.

The relation between temperature and vapor pressure for a three-phase system can be shown by a line on a graph. If, however, we have only two phases, for example a single

hydrate plus water vapor, we have two degrees of freedom, and temperature and pressure can be varied independently of each other over a restricted range. The range of pressures and temperatures for which a particular hydrate is stable is shown by an area on the graph. Figure 6 shows part of the phase diagram for the system $CuSO_4 + H_2O$. So that the different areas may be distinguished clearly, the diagram is not drawn to scale. The curve AP represents the vapor pressure of the saturated solution, that is, the conditions for which solution, pentahydrate, and water vapor are in equilibrium. Curve BP represents the equilibrium $CuSO_4 \cdot 5H_2O$ plus $CuSO_4 \cdot 3H_2O$ plus water vapor. We can call it the graph of the dissociation pressure of the hydrate $CuSO_4 \cdot 5H_2O$. Curve CQ shows the dissociation of $CuSO_4 \cdot 3H_2O$; curve DR, that of $CuSO_4 \cdot H_2O$. The curve $ABCD$ is part of the vapor-pressure curve of ice. When the temperature drops so low that a particular hydrate would have a dissociation pressure higher than the vapor pressure of ice, the hydrate will dissociate into a lower hydrate, or anhydrous salt, plus ice. The areas of stability of the different hydrates are PAB for $CuSO_4 \cdot 5H_2O$, $PBCQ$ for $CuSO_4 \cdot 3H_2O$, and $QCDR$ for $CuSO_4 \cdot H_2O$. Let us use Fig. 6 to guide us in practical preparative problems.

1. At what temperature must we dry copper sulfate in air to get the anhydrous salt?

The average partial vapor pressure of water in the atmosphere is about 10 mm. It will be less on a dry winter's day and more on a humid summer's day. From the curve DR, the dissociation pressure of $CuSO_4 \cdot H_2O$ is 10 mm at 105°. We must therefore dry the salt at 105°, and preferably higher, to be on the safe side. The higher the temperature, the faster the dehydration; but if we heat above 550°, the copper sulfate will lose SO_3 and pass into the basic salt, $CuO \cdot CuSO_4$.

2. Can we prepare anhydrous $CuSO_4$ by drying the hydrates in a desiccator over calcium chloride at room temperature?

At 25°, the partial pressure of water vapor in the system $CaCl_2 \cdot 6H_2O + CaCl_2$ + water vapor is 0.36 mm. From curve D, the dissociation pressure of $CuSO_4 \cdot H_2O$ is 0.04 mm at 25°. We do not, therefore, get anhydrous copper sulfate by drying over calcium chloride at 25°. On the contrary, we could use anhydrous copper sulfate to dehydrate $CaCl_2 \cdot 6H_2O$.

3. How can we prepare pure $CuSO_4 \cdot 3H_2O$?

At 25°, from the curves BP and CQ, this hydrate is stable at water vapor pressures between 5.3 mm and 7.9 mm. If we can control the humidity in a desiccator or closed container to lie between these limits, we can prepare our trihydrate as described below.

Solutions for maintaining constant humidity. A salt in equilibrium with its saturated solution produces a perfectly definite vapor pressure of water at a given temperature. If we want to control the humidity, or the partial pressure of water vapor, in a given space, we can do so by mixing a suitably chosen salt with a little water, so as to give us a mixture of solid salt and saturated solution, and exposing this mixture in the space. Thus in the foregoing example, we can produce a water vapor pressure of 7.14 mm at 24.5° with a mixture of $CaCl_2 \cdot 6H_2O$ and its saturated solution. If we place a lot of moist $CaCl_2 \cdot 6H_2O$ in the bottom chamber of a desiccator and a little $CuSO_4 \cdot 5H_2O$ in the top part of the desiccator, the pentahydrate will slowly lose water and eventually will become the desired $CuSO_4 \cdot 3H_2O$. Another example of this technique is given in Experiment 2 of this manual, where the hydrate $CuCl_2 \cdot 2KCl \cdot 2H_2O$ is dried over moist calcium nitrate, giving a vapor pressure of 8.94 mm at 18.5°. Tables showing the vapor pressures of a number of saturated solutions are available.[6]

Preparation of dry hydrates. A general method to obtain a small specimen of a pure, dry hydrate from a moist product is to take the greater part of the product and dry it

---

[6] See, for example, N. A. Lange, *Handbook of Chemistry*, 6th ed. Handbook Publishers, 1946, pages 1397–1398.

so that about half of it is converted into the anhydrous salt. This is placed in the lower part of a desiccator or wide-mouthed bottle, and above it is placed a smaller portion of the original moist product; the container is closed and set aside for a few days. The moist hydrate will lose water until the last of the saturated solution is gone and the hydrate alone remains, but it will not lose any more moisture thereafter. This method is used in Experiment 2 to obtain a pure specimen of the hydrate of sodium perchlorate, a highly soluble deliquescent salt.

Drying agents. Table 1 shows the drying power of a number of substances commonly used in desiccators and in gas-drying trains. It gives the partial pressure of water

TABLE 1
PRESSURE OF WATER VAPOR ABOVE VARIOUS
DRYING AGENTS AT 25°

P_2O_5	2×10^{-5}	mm
$Mg(ClO_4)_2$	5×10^{-4}	mm
KOH	0.002	mm
Activated alumina	0.003	mm
Concentrated H_2SO_4	0.004	mm
$CaSO_4$ (Drierite)	0.004	mm
CaO	0.2	mm
$CaCl_2$	0.36	mm

vapor each will maintain at room temperature. This table, however, does not give the capacities of the various drying agents. Calcium chloride will take up nearly its own weight of water to form $CaCl_2 \cdot 6H_2O$; but anhydrous calcium sulfate, for example, takes up only 6.6 per cent of its weight of water to form $2CaSO_4 \cdot H_2O$, and the capacity of phosphorus pentoxide is also very low.

When any substance is to be dried in a desiccator, the drying is hastened enormously if the desiccator is evacuated.

CHAPTER IV

Ionic and Covalent Compounds[1]

There are two fundamental types of chemical binding, ionic and covalent. Ionic binding is purely electrostatic and results from the outright transfer of one or more electrons from one atom to another. An example of ionic binding is sodium chloride, or indeed any salt that conducts electricity in the molten or dissolved state. Covalent binding results from the sharing of a pair of electrons between the orbital systems of the two linked atoms. Examples of covalent binding are given by carbon tetrachloride and hydrogen chloride gas.

It is possible for a covalent compound to show some ionic character, and vice versa. For example, the molecule of hydrogen chloride has an electric moment, which means it becomes oriented in an electric field, the hydrogen end of the molecule being positive and chlorine end negative; that is, the binding electrons are not shared equally between the two atoms, the chlorine having a greater share of them than the hydrogen. As we know, the covalent bond between hydrogen and chlorine is broken in a suitable solvent, such as water, which gives H_3O^+ and Cl^-. Studies of electric moments, heats of formation, bond lengths, and other properties have shown that under certain conditions a continuous gradation between extreme ionic and extreme covalent character is possible. Thus the bond H—Cl is considered to have 17 per cent ionic character, and the bond H—F, 60 per cent ionic character. In the prepara-

[1] General references:
N. V. Sidgwick, *The Covalent Link in Chemistry* (1933), especially Chapter 2.
L. Pauling, *The Nature of the Chemical Bond* (1940), especially Chapter 2.

tions described in this manual are a number of chlorides with varying degrees of ionic and covalent character. None the less, the classification of compounds into ionic or covalent according to their type of binding is extremely useful, and most compounds fall fairly definitely into one class or the other.

The difference between ionic and covalent binding leads to characteristic differences in physical and chemical properties. Ionic compounds conduct electricity under conditions where the ions are free to move; covalent compounds do not. The covalent bond is directed in space, but the electrostatic field is not; this leads to important differences in crystal structure. The molecules of a covalent compound are independent entities which have relatively little attraction for one another, but the "molecules" of an ionic compound really have no existence; instead, in an ionic crystal we have a continuous array of charged particles, with alternate positive and negative charges, and the electrical attractions link every part of an ionic crystal to every other part. Therefore a crystal composed of independent covalent molecules is likely to be soft, and the compound will have a low boiling point, while an ionic crystal will be hard and the boiling point will be high. These differences are well illustrated by comparing sodium chloride and carbon tetrachloride:

TABLE 2
IONIC AND COVALENT COMPOUNDS

$NaCl$ (ionic)	CCl_4 (covalent)
Conducts in solution and in molten state	Nonconductor
M.p. 800°, b.p. 1441°	M.p. −23°, b.p. 77°
Hard crystals	Soft waxy crystals in solid state
Crystal lattice close-packed, each Na^+ equidistant from $6Cl^-$	Each C equidistant from 4Cl at corners of tetrahedron, relatively far from other Cl atoms
Soluble in polar solvents, such as H_2O	Soluble in nonpolar solvents, such as hexane

It must be noted that hardness and boiling point are not infallible tests of bond type. The mineral silicates, for example, are very hard and have extremely high boiling points, yet have covalent bonds. These covalent bonds, however, link the atoms into a continuous framework, so that a visible crystal is really one enormous molecule. Then AlF_3, with melting point 1040°, is really not so much more ionic than SiF_4, with melting point $-77°$. Actually, the crystal structures of the two fluorides are different, each fluorine being equidistant from two Al atoms in AlF_3, so that there is a network of forces holding the crystal together in the first case but not in the second.

However, the differences in physical properties between the predominantly ionic chlorides NaCl and $FeCl_2$ and the predominantly covalent chlorides $TiCl_4$ and $FeCl_3$ are plain to see. These, and several other halides having more or less covalent character, are prepared in the experiments to follow. In these compounds the *chemical* properties are found to be related to bond type, too. If an atom forms a covalent bond with chlorine, it will usually, though not invariably, form a stronger covalent bond with oxygen. This statement means that covalent chlorides are generally hydrolyzed by water to give the hydroxide or oxide of the element (and in some cases an oxychloride), together with hydrochloric acid. Thus silicon tetrachloride, which is covalent, reacts completely and irreversibly with water. Titanium tetrachloride (Experiment 18) is hydrolyzed very extensively, but in concentrated solutions not completely. Aluminum bromide and antimony trichloride (Experiments 16 and 20) are intermediate in character, the latter giving an oxychloride with water. Magnesium chloride (Experiment 3) is predominantly ionic and hydrolyzes greatly at high temperatures but very little in the cold. Sodium chloride is not hydrolyzed under any circumstances.

Carbon tetrachloride is an exception, since it does not hydrolyze even though it is covalent. It does not hydrolyze, first, because it is insoluble in water, and second, because the capacity of the carbon atom for coordination is already filled (see below). Mercuric chloride is another exception, since it is ionized very little and yet is not hydrolyzed at all.

Aluminum bromide, incidentally, shows an interesting type of hydrolysis. With a very little water, such as it absorbs on exposure to moist air, it forms an oxybromide that is insoluble in water, and hydrogen bromide is lost. But if enough water is added at the start, it reacts with considerable evolution of heat to give a clear solution that reacts acid to litmus and probably contains colloidal aluminum hydroxide; most of the aluminum, however, is in the form of the very stable hydrated ion $Al(OH_2)_6^{+++}$. The hydrolysis is repressed by the very strong *hydration* of the cation. A similar hydration occurs when stannic chloride dissolves in water (Experiment 19).

THE COVALENCY RULES

Since the type of binding has such an influence upon the physical and chemical properties, rules to help us to anticipate whether a given compound will be ionic or covalent will be extremely useful. Such rules, though only qualitative, are extremely valuable in helping to correlate the properties of elements with their valence numbers and position in the periodic table. There are four covalency rules, the first three being due to Fajans and the fourth to Sidgwick.

Positive and negative ions will be stable in one another's presence only if the attractive forces are not too great. There will always be a deformation of the electron cloud of the negative ion due to the attractive force of the nucleus of the positive ion. If this deformation is large enough, electrons from the outer shell of the anion will be drawn into the orbital system of the cation, and a covalent bond will be set up. The process may be crudely represented as shown in Fig. 7.

By the laws of electrostatics, deformation of the negative ion and hence covalent binding will be favored by the following:

1. High charge on anion or cation.
2. A small cation.
3. A large anion.

The greater the charges the greater the attraction; hence Rule 1. Also the smaller the minimum distance from the positive center of the cation to the outer electrons of the anion the greater the attraction; hence Rule 2. The size of the anion is important, since the deformation of the outer electronic orbits of the anion is *resisted* by the attraction of the nucleus of the anion; the farther away the outer orbits are from the nucleus, that is the larger the anion, the more easily is the ion deformed; hence Rule 3.

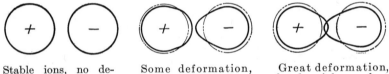

| Stable ions, no deformation | Some deformation, partial covalent character | Great deformation, bond mainly covalent |

Fig. 7. Deformation of ions.

There is a fourth effect that has to do with the way in which the electronic orbits are arranged. It is well known that the most stable arrangements of the electrons in atoms are found in the inert gases. An ion like the potassium ion, where the electrons are arranged in shells just as are the electrons of the argon atom, is much more stable and is harder to reduce than the cuprous ion, for example, where the electronic arrangement is *not* that of an inert gas. This condition is shown most simply by referring to the ionization potentials of the gaseous atoms, which are 7.68 volts for Cu and only 4.32 volts for K (for the loss of the first electron in each case). The electron configurations of K, Cu, and A are as follows:

K (atom) [19] 2.8.8.1   Cu (atom) [29] 2.8.18.1
K$^+$ (ion) [19] 2.8.8   Cu$^+$ (ion) [29] 2.8.18
A (atom) [18] 2.8.8

"Inert-gas-type" ions, such as K^+, Ca^{++}, La^{+++}, are much more stable than "noninert-gas-type" ions, such as Cu^+, Ag^+, Zn^{++}, Ga^{+++}. This statement is true for the ease of reduction to the metal, measured either by the ionization potentials or by the standard electrode potentials, and it is also true for the ease of forming covalent bonds. Atoms whose ions would be of the noninert-gas type are more prone to form covalent bonds, other things being equal, than those which give inert-gas-type ions. Many complex ions and covalent compounds of Cu^+, Ag^+, and Zn^{++} are known, but very few of Na^+, K^+, and Ca^{++}. Thus the fourth covalency rule reads:

4. Ionic linkage is favored if the ions have electronic configurations like those of the inert gases.

Examples of the application of the covalency rules are given in Table 3. The boiling points of the compounds chosen for comparison are quoted, since boiling point is a convenient rough and ready indication of bond type; but the ionic or covalent character is also shown by electrical conductivity, reaction with water, and other properties.

TABLE 3
THE COVALENCY RULES

Covalency favored by	Examples
1. High ionic charge	CCl_4 (b.p. 77°) vs. NaCl (b.p. 1441°)
	$FeCl_3$ (b.p. 315°) vs. $FeCl_2$ (b.p. 1000°)
2. Small cation	$BeCl_2$ (b.p. 520°) vs. $CaCl_2$ (b.p. 1600°); equivalent conductances in molten condition, $BeCl_2$ 0.09, $MgCl_2$ 28.8, $CaCl_2$ 51.9
3. Large anion	I_3^-, HgI_4^- more stable than Cl_3^-, $HgCl_4^-$; AgI can have covalent crystal lattice, AgCl not
4. Noninert gas structure of ion	$CdCl_2$ (b.p. 960°) vs. $CaCl_2$ (b.p. 1600°)
	AgI vs. KI, $Pb(NO_3)_2$ vs. $Ca(NO_3)_2$

There are a few exceptions to the covalency rules, such as the case of mercuric chloride and mercuric salts in general, which are far less ionized than the corresponding salts of zinc or cadmium despite the large size of the mercury atom. Nevertheless, these rules are extremely useful in correlating the facts of inorganic chemistry. Which, for instance, should be the stronger base, $Cr(OH)_2$ or $Cr(OH)_3$? Chrom*ous* hydroxide, $Cr(OH)_2$, because the smaller charge of the chromous ion as compared with the chromic ion makes it less liable to enter into covalent linkage with oxygen. It is universally true, with no exceptions, that when any element has more than one oxidation state and forms a number of hydroxides, the basic strength of the hydroxide decreases as the positive charge on the cation increases. One can go further and extend the rule to the acidic strength of acidic oxides and oxyacids. Subject to certain reservations mentioned in the next paragraph, as the positive oxidation number increases, the strength of the corresponding oxyacid increases. Thus perchloric acid is a stronger acid than chloric, arsenic acid is stronger than arsenious, selenic acid is stronger than selenious (see Experiment 37). The element manganese in its various oxidation states shows the whole range from the strongly basic hydroxide of Mn^{+2} to the strong acid formed by Mn^{+7}; see Table 4.

TABLE 4

OXIDATION STATES OF MANGANESE

Oxidation number	Predominating ion or oxide	Acidic or basic character of hydroxide
+2	Mn^{++}	Strong base
+3	Mn^{+++}	Weak base
+4	MnO_2	Very feebly basic and acidic
+6	MnO_4^-	Weak acid
+7	MnO_4^-	Strong acid

However, the strength of oxyacids does not depend only on the oxidation state of the central atom, but on structural factors as well. For example, the acid H_3PO_3, in which one hydrogen atom is attached directly to the phosphorus and cannot ionize, is somewhat stronger than H_3PO_4, in spite of the lower oxidation number of the phosphorus, $+3$ as compared with $+5$; the first ionization constants are 1.6×10^{-2} and 7.5×10^{-3}, respectively. The acid $H_4P_2O_7$

with $K_1 = 1.4 \times 10^{-1}$ is stronger than either of them; this condition is characteristic of acids with more than one "central atom" in the molecule. A good rule covering the strengths of oxyacids with only one "central atom" is the "formal charge" rule.[2] The "formal charge" is the charge on the ion of the fully ionized acid plus the number of oxygen atoms attached to the central atom. Thus in $SO_4^=$, the formal charge of the sulfur is $-2 + 4 = +2$. For ClO_4^- the formal charge of the chlorine is $-1 + 4 = +3$. For $HPO_3^=$, the anion of phosphorous acid, the formal charge of the phosphorus is $-2 + 3 = +1$. The rule now states:

Formal charge	Value of K_1	Example
0	10^{-7} approximately	$HClO$
+1	10^{-2} approximately	H_2SO_3
+2	10^3 approximately	H_2SO_4
+3	Very large indeed	$HClO_4$

To return to the covalency rules; the effect of *ionic size* on the basic strength of hydroxides is illustrated again and again. For example, in the rare-earth series, which is the strongest base, $La(OH)_3$ or $Lu(OH)_3$? Lanthanum hydroxide is the strongest base and lutecium hydroxide the weakest, because La^{+++} has the largest radius of the trivalent rare-earth ions and Lu^{+++} has the smallest. The progressive decrease of basic strength with decreasing ionic radius (and increasing atomic number) is used in separating the rare-earth elements from one another.

Not only degrees of ionization but also the stabilities of compounds can be correlated by means of the covalency rules. Taking as an example the decomposition of the carbonates by heat, Na_2CO_3 decomposes only very slightly at a white heat, $CaCO_3$ decomposes completely into CaO and CO_2 at a bright-red heat, and $Al_2(CO_3)_3$ is very difficult to prepare at all. We can visualize the decomposition as

[2] See W. M. Latimer, *Oxidation Potentials*. New York: Prentice-Hall, 1938, page vi. Also L. Pauling , *General Chemistry*. San Francisco: Freeman and Company, 1947, page 394.

proceeding by the positive ion attracting an oxygen atom away from the carbon of the carbonate, thus:

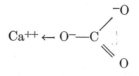

The larger the charge of the cation and the smaller its size, the greater will be the attraction. For an illustration of the effects of the radius of the cation, let us select the group Mg-Ca-Sr-Ba and compare the temperatures at which the dissociation pressure of carbon dioxide equals 1 atmosphere. The smaller the cation, the more easily the carbonate decomposes:

TABLE 5

DECOMPOSITION TEMPERATURES
OF CARBONATES

$MgCO_3$	542°
$CaCO_3$	882°
$SrCO_3$	1155°
$BaCO_3$	1360°

Such facts are important in preparative chemistry. If dolomitic limestone, containing $MgCO_3$ and $CaCO_3$, is carefully heated, the $MgCO_3$ can be completely decomposed to MgO without affecting the $CaCO_3$; the resulting mass has certain absorptive properties and is used for removing small amounts of dissolved silicates from boiler feed water. If we wish to prepare BaO from barium carbonate, we cannot simply heat it in a muffle furnace as we heat calcium carbonate to get CaO; the temperature is not high enough. The best procedure is to heat the barium carbonate strongly in a crucible with powdered carbon, which will combine with the carbon dioxide to form carbon monoxide and so allow the decomposition to proceed.

The decomposition of other oxysalts, such as nitrates and sulfates, follows the same rules. Barium sulfate can be heated to bright redness without decomposition, as the analytical chemist knows; calcium sulfate loses some SO_3

at a bright-red heat to form a basic sulfate, or mixture of oxide and sulfate, which makes a good plaster; the sulfates of tripositive Fe, Al, and Cr lose their SO_3 below a red heat; in fact, the first fuming sulfuric acid to be manufactured, (Nordhausen sulfuric acid), was made with sulfur trioxide formed by heating ferric sulfate. The ease of decomposition of the hydroxides and peroxides depends upon the size and charge of the cation in exactly the same way.

CHAPTER V

Coordination Compounds and Complex Ions

COORDINATION COMPOUNDS

Coordination compounds are formed by the union of two or more compounds which are themselves stable and capable of independent existence. Some of them dissociate on heating, but others are extremely stable. Examples of coordination compounds are NH_3BF_3 (Experiment 15), $A(BF_3)_2$, $Fe(CO)_5$, $Co(NH_3)_3(NO_2)_3$, and ionized salts such as $Cu(NH_3)_4SO_4$ (Experiment 5), $K_4Fe(CN)_6$, the hundreds of cobaltammines, NH_4Cl, and H_2SiF_6. These compounds were a puzzle to the older theories of valence, since their formation seemed to involve residual valences or valences in excess of the normal valences of the atoms concerned. Today, however, they are believed to be bound by means of the coordinate link, which is simply a special kind of covalent bond.

It takes two electrons spinning in opposite directions to form a covalent bond. Normally, one of these electrons is contributed by each of the two atoms being linked, but it can also happen that both of the binding electrons come from the same atom. Where this is the case, the link is said to be a *coordinate link*. We can formulate coordination compounds on the Lewis notation as follows:

In these diagrams, crosses represent electrons that are originally from nitrogen, hydrogen, or oxygen atoms. It will be noted that the sulfate ion can be formulated as a coordination compound, although it has a much greater stability than, for example, the ion $[Cu(NH_3)_4]^{++}$, which dissociates into Cu^{++} and $4NH_3$ on heating.

A less cumbersome method of representing the coordinate link is to draw an arrow pointing in the direction in which the pair of electrons is donated, thus:

$$H_3N \rightarrow BF_3 \qquad \left[\begin{array}{c} NH_3 \\ \downarrow \\ H_3N \rightarrow Cu \leftarrow NH_3 \\ \uparrow \\ NH_3 \end{array} \right]^{++}$$

The coordinate link is, of course, electrically unsymmetrical and has considerable ionic character; hence the names "semipolar bond" and "coionic link," which are also used for this type of binding. Molecules containing the coordinate link usually show a pronounced electrical dipole moment; that is, they will tend to turn and orient themselves when they are placed in an electric field just as a compass needle orients itself in a magnetic field.

Very many coordination compounds are known between metal atoms and bifunctional organic molecules, where the binding is partly normal covalent links and partly coordinate links; for example, copper acetate solution mixed with acetylacetone gives a blue compound that is non-ionized and can be vaporized unchanged. It can be formulated:

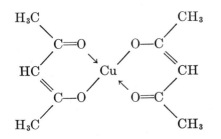

Such compounds containing closed rings in which one or both of the linkages with the metal atom are coordinate links are known as *chelate compounds*, from the Greek *chela*, a crab's claw. Chelate compounds are numerous and are important in analytical chemistry. The familiar red precipitate obtained from dimethylglyoxime and an ammoniacal solution of a nickel salt is a chelate compound having the structure

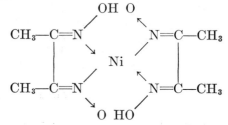

In these formulas it must be understood that there is resonance between single and double bonds. The formulas could equally well have been written with the coordinate links at lower left and upper right, and the four valence bonds of the metals are indistinguishable in practice.

COMPLEX IONS

Complex ions are any ions that are built up by the union of simpler ions, or of an ion and one or more neutral molecules. They are usually formed around metallic ions. They may be held together entirely by coordinate links, as in $Cu(NH_3)_4^{++}$ and the other metal-ammonia complexes, or they may be bound by a combination of coordinate links and normal covalent links, as in $HgI_4^=$ or $Fe(CN)_6^{\equiv}$. They may even be held together by purely ionic or electrostatic forces, as is the case in $FeF_6^{\equiv}$; this complex is shown by its large magnetic moment to contain a free ferric ion, yet it is extremely stable, since the small size of the fluoride ion allows for close approach and a strong electrostatic force between Fe^{+++} and F^-.

Complex ions are known both in the solid and in the dissolved states. In solution they dissociate to some extent, but this dissociation may be extremely small. Thus in dilute acid solution the salt $K_4Fe(CN)_6$ gives none of the reactions of cyanides and none of the reactions of ferrous ion. The complex ferric salt $K_3Fe(C_2O_4)_3$ (Experiment 9) gives only a very feeble coloration with thiocyanate and does not deposit ferric oxide when dilute ammonia is added. Such masking or modification of reactions by complex-ion formation is extremely useful in analytical chemistry and often in preparative chemistry also.

A complex salt is to be distinguished from a double salt such as ferric alum (ferric ammonium sulfate). Double salts exist only in the solid state, and then only because the different constituent ions happen to fit into a common crystal lattice. In solution, double salts give all the reactions of their constituent simple ions (Experiment 4).

Complex ions of metals are extremely numerous. They vary in stability all the way from the unstable $Mg(NH_3)_6^{++}$, whose existence and formula are manifested only by a careful study of the vapor pressure of ammonia in solutions containing magnesium salts, to the very stable $Fe(CN)_6^{\equiv}$ and $Co(NH_3)_6^{+++}$. In complexity they vary from $HgCl^+$ and $Ag(CN)_2^-$ to the ions of the important heteropoly acids, one of which is $H_3[PO_4(MoO_3)_{12}]$. The metals that form the most numerous complex ions are those of the iron-platinum group and chromium; the alkali and alkaline earth metals form the fewest complexes. Metals of B subgroups, such as Cu, Zn, and Pb, form more complex ions than their counterparts in the A subgroups, as we should expect from the covalency rules (see Chapter IV). The effect of the size and charge of the metal ion on the stability of its complexes is usually that which we should expect from the covalency rules.

The ions and molecules that attach themselves to metallic ions to form complexes are those with a more or less pronounced electronegative character, such as NH_3, H_2O, NO, CN^-, NO_2^-, $C_2O_4^=$, Cl^-, F^-. The size of the atom or ion also affects its ability to coordinate; thus fluoride ions, being small, can cluster around other atoms and form complex ions (examples: BF_4^-, $AlF_6^=$, $SiF_6^=$) where the chloride ion would be too large to fit. We must also note the complex-forming ability of phosphate ions, especially the more complicated phosphate ions such as the anion of sodium hexametaphosphate. This ability is quite exceptional, and the complex ions of phosphates with metals are unique in their constitutions and properties (see Experiment 29).

Experiment 9 includes tests to explore the relative stabilities of a number of complexes of ferric ion.

Coordination number. The number of atoms that can be grouped around a central atom in a complex compound is known as the *coordination number* of the central atom. It bears little or no relation to the oxidation state of the central atom or the vertical column of the periodic table into which it falls, but is determined rather by the horizontal row of the periodic table in which the element is included. In the first short period (Li to F) the coordination number is never greater than 4. Thus beryllium forms complex ions $BeF_4^=$, $Be(NH_3)_4^{++}$, $Be(C_2O_4)_2^=$, and so on, but not $BeF_6^=$, $Be(NH_3)_6^{++}$, and so on. Boron likewise forms the ion BF_4^- but never $BF_6^=$, and in the coordination compound BF_3NH_3 mentioned above, its coordination number is 4. In carbon, the coordination number and the oxidation number are the same; probably this fact accounts for the variety and stability of compounds of tetravalent carbon. 4-Coordinated nitrogen is known in the ammonium ion and in complex ions containing ammonia; 4-coordinated oxygen is rather rare but is known in $Be_4O \cdot (CH_3COO)_6$, for example. 4-Coordinated fluorine is not known.

In the second short period and the first long period, the maximum coordination number is 6. $SiF_6^=$ and the very stable SF_6 are examples from the second short period, but only the fluoride ion is small enough to form stable 6-coordinated compounds in this period. In the first long period we have many more examples, such as the 6-coordinated complexes of chromium, iron, and cobalt. Nevertheless, some elements seem content with a smaller coordination number, for example nickel, copper and zinc, with coordination numbers of four. In the second and third long period, higher coordination numbers sometimes appear, as in $TaF_8^=$ and $Mo(CN)_8^=$.

The coordination number is related partly to the radius of the atom, but also to the number of electrons which the atom can hold (according to quantum theory) in its outermost shell. In the first short period the maximum number of electrons the outer shell can hold is 8, so that higher coordination numbers than 4 are impossible. In the second short period the outer electron shell has principal quantum number 3 and can hold up to 18 electrons. A coordination number of 9 is theoretically possible, but the limitations of physical space prevent the coordination number from being higher than 6. The difference in coordination maximum between the two short periods has interesting chemical consequences; for example, CCl_4 is not hydrolyzed by water, yet $SiCl_4$ is hydrolyzed very rapidly. It is possible for a water molecule to coordinate onto the silicon, thus: $H_2O \rightarrow SiCl_4$, whereas no such coordination is possible with CCl_4; this difference may explain the difference in behavior of the two chlorides.

Stereochemistry. From considerations of symmetry, 6-coordinated complexes are expected to be octahedral in shape, and the evidence indicates that they are so (see the discussion in Experiment 10). 4-Coordinated complexes of the first short period are tetrahedral, as we should expect, and the same is true of most other 4-coordinated complexes. However, 4-coordinated nickel, palladium, platinum, cupric copper, and argentic silver show a planar distribution of valences.

Bond orbitals and stereochemistry. The number and direction of the valence bonds in compounds depends on the particular electron orbitals which form the bonds. The principles may be seen by referring to 6-coordinated cobalt, planar 4-coordinated nickel, and tetrahedral 4-coordinated beryllium as examples.   The electrons are distributed in orbits as follows:

Co^{+++}:	$1s^2$	$2s^2$	$2p^6$	$3s^2$	$3p^6$	$3d^6$		
Co in Co(NH$_3$)$_6$$^{+++}$:	$1s^2$	$2s^2$	$2p^6$	$3s^2$	$3p^6$	$3d^{10}$	$4s^2$	$4p^6$
Bonding electrons:						$3d^4$	$4s^2$	$4p^6$
Ni^{++}:	$1s^2$	$2s^2$	$2p^6$	$3s^2$	$3p^6$	$3d^8$		
Ni in Ni(CN)$_4$$^=$:	$1s^2$	$2s^2$	$2p^6$	$3s^2$	$3p^6$	$3d^{10}$	$4s^2$	$4p^4$
Bonding electrons:						$3d^2$	$4s^2$	$4p^4$
Be^{++}:	$1s^2$							
Be in Be(NH$_3$)$_4$$^{++}$:	$1s^2$	$2s^2$	$2p^6$					
Bonding electrons:		$2s^2$	$2p^6$					

A pair of electrons goes to each orbital.   In the hybridization of the orbitals according to quantum-mechanical principles, the two d, one s, and three p orbitals of the first example combine to give six bonds arranged octahedrally; in the second example, one d, one s, and two p orbitals combine to give four planar bonds; in the third example, one s and three p orbitals together give tetrahedral bonds.

These generalizations hold good for normal covalent bonds as well as coordinate bonds, for there is no fundamental difference between the two.   It is interesting to note that Ni(CO)$_4$, containing 4-covalent nickel, is tetrahedral, not planar, because the $3d$ orbitals are all filled and the bonding is done through one $4s$ and three $4p$ orbitals.

CHAPTER VI

Oxidation and Reduction

Up to now we have used the terms "valence" and "oxidation number" without defining them explicitly in a quantitative sense. In the discussion to follow we shall understand "valence" in the quantitative sense to mean the number of bonds that link an atom to its neighbors. By "oxidation number" we shall mean the number of electrons that must be removed from each atom of the free element to form the compound under consideration, subject to the convention that combined oxygen shall have an oxidation number of -2 (except in peroxycompounds) and that covalently bound hydrogen shall have an oxidation number of $+1$. In the ion $[Co(NH_3)_6]^{+++}$, for example, cobalt is 6-covalent and has an oxidation number of $+3$.

Reactions in which a change of oxidation number occurs are known as *oxidation-reduction reactions*. They are very numerous in inorganic chemistry and very important. A simple example of an oxidation-reduction reaction is

$$2FeCl_2 + Cl_2 \rightarrow 2FeCl_3$$

The iron gains in positive charge from $+2$ to $+3$, and is said to be oxidized; the chlorine that combines with the ferrous chloride changes from an oxidation number of zero in free chlorine to one of -1 in ferric chloride. Generally, we define oxidation and reduction as follows:

A substance is *oxidized* when it gains in oxidation number or loses electrons. An *oxidizing agent* removes electrons from other substances.

A substance is *reduced* when it loses in oxidation number or gains electrons. A *reducing agent* supplies electrons to other substances.

43

The term "oxidation" originally meant, simply, combination with oxygen, as in $2C + O_2 \rightarrow 2CO$, $2CO + O_2 \rightarrow 2CO_2$, or $2Fe + 3O_2 \rightarrow Fe_2O_3$. However, the last reaction is very similar to $2Fe + 3Cl_2 \rightarrow 2FeCl_3$ and to $2FeCl_2 + Cl_2 \rightarrow 2FeCl_3$. The conversion of ferrous chloride to ferric chloride can, moreover, be accomplished by gaseous oxygen, if oxygen is bubbled through a solution of ferrous chloride containing hydrochloric acid. Hence the extension of the term "oxidation" to cover any increase in combining power associated with loss of electrons. The term "reduction" in its original chemical sense meant the reduction of a metallic ore to the metal, as in $Fe_2O_3 + 3CO \rightarrow 2Fe + 3CO_2$; but the reaction $2FeCl_3 + H_2 \rightarrow 2FeCl_2 + 2HCl$ is so similar that it, too, must be described as the *reduction* of ferric chloride.

The description of oxidation and reduction in terms of electron losses and gains is not merely formal, since very many oxidations and reductions can be carried out by means of an electric current, and in fact are so carried out (see Chapter VII, Electrolytic Methods). If a ferric chloride solution is electrolyzed between inert electrodes, such as platinum, the ferric ion is reduced to ferrous at the cathode:

$$Fe^{+++} + e \rightarrow Fe^{++}$$

whereas at the anode, chloride ion is oxidized to chlorine:

$$Cl^- \rightarrow \tfrac{1}{2}Cl_2 + e$$

The external source of electromotive force—the dynamo or battery—serves as a "pump" to draw the electrons out from the anode into the external circuit and deliver them to the cathode. We note, in passing, that whenever one substance is oxidized, another is simultaneously reduced; the number of electrons lost by the substance or substances oxidized must always equal the number gained by the substance or substances reduced. This fact is used in balancing oxidation-reduction equations.

Of course, not all oxidations and reductions involve ions,

and these are difficult or impossible to perform in an electrolytic cell, for example $2CO + O_2 \rightarrow 2CO_2$. But even here it is perhaps permissible to speak of the carbon of carbon monoxide as "donating electrons" to the second oxygen when it forms carbon dioxide, since it shares two of its electrons with this oxygen to form a double covalent bond. For cases like this it is perhaps preferable to speak of gains and losses of oxidation number.

OXIDATION-REDUCTION POTENTIALS

It is common knowledge that in order for a reaction to "go," or proceed of its own accord, it must be capable of performing useful work. This ability follows from the second law of thermodynamics, which says in effect that work can pass spontaneously and completely into heat (for example, when the output of an engine is lost in friction), whereas heat cannot be transformed spontaneously into work. It is not necessary for a reaction to be exothermic, or to give out heat, in order to "go"; in fact, some spontaneous reactions are endothermic. But it *must* be capable of providing useful work, or it will not take place of its own accord. The useful work or "free energy" that a reaction can provide is a measure of its power, or tendency to "go."

It is easy to measure this free energy in reactions that transfer electrons, since these electrons can be harnessed to give an electric current. The power of an electric current to do work depends upon the voltage (or *electromotive force*) under which it is produced, and electromotive force can be very exactly measured. Suppose we want to know the free energy of the reaction

$$Zn + CuSO_4 \text{ (solution)} \rightarrow ZnSO_4 \text{ (solution)} + Cu$$

We set up a cell of the following form:

| Metallic zinc | ZnSO₄ solution | CuSO₄ solution | Metallic copper |

Zinc dips into zinc sulfate solution, copper dips into copper sulfate solution, and the two solutions are separated by a porous pot or by a narrow tube to give electrical contact but to impede their mixing. We find that the zinc becomes the negative pole of the cell, from which electrons are sent out into the external circuit when the cell supplies electricity, whereas the copper becomes the positive pole. The electromotive force is about 1.1 volt, the exact value depending on the concentrations of the solutions and to some extent on the temperature. If iron, which is known to be a weaker reducing agent than zinc, is substituted for the zinc in this cell, and ferrous sulfate is substituted for zinc sulfate, the electromotive force is only 0.8 volt, showing that the free energy of the reaction

$$Fe + CuSO_4 \text{ (solution)} \rightarrow FeSO_4 \text{ (solution)} + Cu$$

is less, for the same number of electrons transferred, than that of the reaction between zinc and cupric ions.

The oxidizing and reducing powers of substances that form ions are generally referred to hydrogen as standard. An electrode can be set up in which hydrogen gas bubbles over a piece of platinum foil coated with finely divided platinum and dipping into a dilute solution of a strong acid. The platinum catalyzes the reaction

$$2H^+ + 2e \rightleftharpoons H_2$$

and at the same time serves to conduct the electrons in or out of the cell. If, now, the hydrogen pressure and the acid concentration are standardized, we have a standard half cell, which can be combined with any desired half cell, e.g. copper metal in copper sulfate solutions, to measure the strength of the oxidation-reduction reaction in this half cell. For example, the cell

$$Zn \mid ZuSO_4 \text{ (1M)} \mid HCl \text{ (1M)} \mid H_2 \text{ (1 atm)}, Pt$$

has an electromotive force of 0.76 volt, the hydrogen electrode being positive. This measures the force of the reaction

$$Zn + 2H^+ \text{ (1M)} \rightarrow Zn^{++} \text{ (1M)} + H_2 \text{ (1 atm}$$

and since hydrogen is taken the standard, we can write simply

$$\text{Zn} \rightarrow \text{Zn}^{++} + 2e, \qquad E_H^0 = +0.76 \text{ volt}$$

The superscript "0" means that the zinc metal and zinc ions are in their standard states, that is, pure zinc metal and a zinc salt of unit activity (approximately 1-molar). The subscript "H" means that the standard hydrogen electrode has been chosen as reference. We shall omit this subscript hereafter, since all our potentials will be expressed on the standard hydrogen scale.

For the reaction $\text{Cu} \rightarrow \text{Cu}^{++} + 2e$,

$$E^0 = -0.34 \text{ volt}$$

Therefore if we combine the standard zinc and copper electrodes directly, as was done above, we shall have an electromotive force that is the algebraic difference between $+0.76$ and -0.34, namely, 1.10 volt.

The oxidation-reduction potentials for half reactions such as $\text{Fe}^{++} \rightarrow \text{Fe}^{+++} + e$ are measured by putting a piece of platinum or other inert metal into a solution containing ferrous and ferric ions in standard concentrations, and combining this half cell with the standard hydrogen half cell. Again, the platinum serves to conduct electrons and to catalyze the equilibrium between ferrous and ferric ions. The electromotive force of the cell

$$\text{Pt} \mid \text{Fe}^{++} (1M), \text{Fe}^{+++} (1M) \mid \text{H}^+ (1M) \mid \text{H}_2 (1 \text{ atm}), \text{Pt}$$

is 0.75 volt, the hydrogen this time being the negative pole; and so we write

$$\text{Fe}^{++} \rightarrow \text{Fe}^{+++} + e, \qquad E^0 = -0.75 \text{ volt}$$

Table 6, Oxidation-Reduction Potentials at 25°, appears on page 48.

Convention of signs. In the above examples the standard American convention set by Lewis and Randall has been used. That is, the electrode potential is considered positive if the standard hydrogen electrode in a completed cell would be the positive pole. The opposite convention is usually used in the European literature; the standard potential of the ferrous-ferric system would be called $+0.75$ volt, because in a cell with the hydrogen electrode, the electrode dipping into the ferrous and ferric salts would

TABLE 6

OXIDATION-REDUCTION POTENTIALS AT 25°

Reaction	E^0 (Volts)[1]
$K \rightarrow K^+ + e$	$+2.92$
$Ca \rightarrow Ca^{++} + 2e$	$+2.76$
$Na \rightarrow Na^+ + e$	$+2.71$
$Mg \rightarrow Mg^{++} + e$	$+1.87$
$Zn \rightarrow Zn^{++} + 2e$	$+0.762$
$Cr \rightarrow Cr^{++} + 2e$	$+0.557$
$Fe \rightarrow Fe^{++} + 2e$	$+0.441$
$Cr^{++} \rightarrow Cr^{+++} + e$	$+0.400$
$Co \rightarrow Co^{++} + 2e$	$+0.29$
$Ni \rightarrow Ni^{++} + 2e$	$+0.23$
$Sn \rightarrow Sn^{++} + 2e$	$+0.136$
$Pb \rightarrow Pb^{++} + 2e$	$+0.122$
$H_2 \rightarrow 2H^+ + 2e$	$+0.000$
$H_2O + Ti^{+++} \rightarrow TiO^{++} + 2H^+ + 2e$	-0.1
$Sn^{++} \rightarrow Sn^{++++} + 2e$	-0.13
$Cu^+ \rightarrow Cu^{++} + e$	-0.17
$Cu \rightarrow Cu^{++} + 2e$	-0.344
$Fe(CN)_6^{\equiv} \rightarrow Fe(CN)_6^{\equiv} + e$	-0.487
$2I^- \rightarrow I_2 + 2e$	-0.535
$H_2O \rightarrow H_3AsO_3 \rightarrow H_3AsO_4 + 2H^+ + 2e$	-0.574
$MnO_4^- \rightarrow MnO_4^- + e$	-0.664
$Fe^{++} \rightarrow Fe^{+++} + e$	-0.748
$2CNS^- \rightarrow (CNS)_2 + 2e$	-0.77
$Ag \rightarrow Ag^+ + e$	-0.798
$2Hg \rightarrow Hg_2^{++} + 2e$	-0.799
$H_2O + ClO_3^- \rightarrow ClO_4^- + 2H^+ + 2e$	-1.00
$2Br^- \rightarrow Br_2 + 2e$	-1.065
$H_2O + H_2SeO_3 \rightarrow SeO_4^- + 4H^+ + 2e$	-1.15
$6H_2O + I_2 \rightarrow 2IO_3^- + 12H^+ + 10e$	-1.197
$2H_2O \rightarrow O_2 + 4H^+ + 4e$	-1.23
$2Cl^- \rightarrow Cl_2 + 2e$	-1.358
$7H_2O + 2Cr^{+++} \rightarrow Cr_2O_7^- + 14H^+ + 6e$	-1.36
$6H_2O + Cl_2 \rightarrow 2ClO_2^- + 12H^+ + 10e$	-1.47
$4H_2O + Mn^{++} \rightarrow MnO_4^- + 8H^+ + 5e$	-1.52
$2H_2O \rightarrow H_2O_2 + 2H^+ + 2e$	-1.77
$Co^{++} \rightarrow Co^{+++} + e$	-1.84
$Ag^+ \rightarrow Ag^{++} + e$	-1.98
$2SO_4^- \rightarrow S_2O_8^- + 2e$	-2.05
$2F^- \rightarrow F_2 + 2e$	-2.85

[1] Many of these values are taken from the table in Latimer and Hildebrand, *Reference Book of Inorganic Chemistry*. New York: Macmillan, 1940.

be the positive, withdrawing electrons from the external circuit.

Following the conventional notation of Lewis and Randall[2] we write the electrons on the right-hand side of the equation, thus:

$$X \rightarrow X^+ + e$$

A positive value for the electrode potential then signifies that X will spontaneously give up electrons to hydrogen ions under standard conditions, that is to say, X will liberate hydrogen from a dilute acid.

Effect of concentration. Obviously, a reaction will proceed more readily if the products are dilute and the reactants concentrated. This condition is expressed quantitatively by the Nernst equation:

$$E = E^0 + \frac{RT}{nF} \ln \frac{(\text{activity of reactants})}{(\text{activity of products})}$$

where R = the gas constant

T = absolute temperature

F = the faraday = 96,490 coulombs per gram equivalent

n = number of electrons transferred in the equation as written

The *activities* are the effective concentrations, defined with reference to their effect on free energy. The activity of a pure solid, or of pure liquid water, is taken as unity. For a dissolved substance, the activity is unity when the solute produces the same effect as it would in a 1-molal solution which obeys the laws of the ideal solution. For our purposes, we can take the activity as equal to the molar concentration without much error.

The activities in the Nernst equation must be raised to the same power as the number of molecules taking part in the equation as written, thus:

[2] *Thermodynamics.* New York: McGraw-Hill, 1923, page 402.

$$\text{Fe}^{++} \rightarrow \text{Fe}^{+++} + \text{e}, \qquad E = -0.75 + \frac{RT}{F} \ln \frac{a_{\text{Fe}^{++}}}{a_{\text{Fe}^{+++}}}$$

$$2\text{H}_2\text{O} \rightarrow 4\text{H}^+ + \text{O}_2 + 4\text{e}, \qquad E = -1.33 + \frac{RT}{4F} \ln \frac{a_{\text{H}_2\text{O}}{}^2}{a_{\text{H}^+}{}^4 a_{\text{O}_2}}$$

Since the activities, or concentrations, enter as the logarithm it takes a very large change of concentration to make much difference to the electrode potential or to the free energy of the reaction. For preparative inorganic chemistry we rarely have to take account of concentrations in deciding whether a particular reaction is possible, unless the reaction involves hydrogen or hydroxyl ions. The concentrations of these ions may vary over many powers of 10, and a reaction that goes well in alkaline solution may be quite impossible in acid solution, or vice versa.

Examples of the use of oxidation-reduction potentials in preparative chemistry:

(a) *The preparation of chromous salts.* E^0 for $\text{Cr}^{++} \rightarrow \text{Cr}^{+++} + \text{e}$ is $+0.41$ volt. That is, if we are to find a reducing agent which will effectively reduce chromic salts to chromous in aqueous solutions, we must look for a reducing agent having an E^0 of at least $+0.5$ volt, to give enough margin for effective reaction. From the table, zinc, with E^0 for $\text{Zn} \rightarrow \text{Zn}^{++} + 2\text{e} = +0.76$ volt is the least active metal that can be used, other than chromium itself. Iron, with E^0 for $\text{Fe} \rightarrow \text{Fe}^{++} + 2\text{e} = +0.44$ volt, would react only incompletely (see Experiment 45).

(b) *The preparation of salts of dipositive silver,* Ag^{++}. E^0 for $\text{Ag}^+ \rightarrow \text{Ag}^{++} + \text{e}$ is -1.98 volt. Stronger oxidizing agents are fluorine $(2\text{F}^- \rightarrow \text{F}_2 + 2\text{e}, \ E^0 = -2.85$ volt$)$ and peroxydisulfates $(2\text{SO}_4{}^= \rightarrow \text{S}_2\text{O}_8{}^= + 2\text{e}, \ E^0 = -2.05$ volt$)$. Peroxydisulfates seem hardly strong enough, but if the activity of the resulting Ag^{++} is lowered sufficiently by making it into a complex ion with pyridine, a complete reaction is possible (see Experiment 48, Test 5).

(c) *The preparation of chromates.* E^0 for $2\text{Cr}^{+++} + 7\text{H}_2\text{O} \rightarrow \text{Cr}_2\text{O}_7{}^= + 14\text{H}^+ + 6\text{e}$ is -1.36 volt. This value means that hexapositive chromium is more powerfully oxidizing than gaseous oxygen, since E^0 for $2H_2O \rightarrow 4H^+ + O_2 + 4e$ is only -1.23 volt. However, both half reactions involve the hydrogen ion, and the chromium reaction is a good deal more sensitive to hydrogen-ion concentration than is the oxygen reaction, as the Nernst equation will show. From the Nernst equation the potentials of the two half reactions become equal if a_{H^+} is reduced from 1-molar to 0.04-molar, other activities remaining standard. So it is no wonder that in neutral or alkaline solution tripositive chromium can easily be oxidized to chromate by atmospheric oxygen (Experiment 35).

THE OXIDATION STATES OF THE ELEMENTS

There are three groups of elements that show two or more oxidation states. The first includes the transition metals and in the first long period takes in Ti, V, Cr, Mn, Fe, Co, Ni, and Cu. The second includes B subgroup elements of the third, fourth, fifth, and possibly sixth groups: In, Tl, Ge, Sn, Pb, As, Sb, Bi, Se, Te. The third group includes the nonmetals: nitrogen, phosphorus, sulfur, and the halogens.

The transition metals are distinguished by having two incomplete electron shells in their atoms. For example, the element vanadium, with atomic number 23, has the electronic arrangement (23) 2. 8. 11. 2. The outer pair of electrons in the $4s$ level enter into chemical combination very easily and can be lost outright to form the vanadous ion, V^{++}. The 11 electrons in the third shell are grouped as follows: two $3s$, six $3p$, three $3d$. The three $3d$ electrons have the highest potential energies in this shell and can be lost or shared in chemical combination. The atom can give up one, two, or all three of these, giving oxidation states of 3, 4, or 5. (In the higher oxidation states, electrons are shared rather than lost outright; thus the cation of tetrapositive vanadium in aqueous solution is VO^{++}, not V^{++++}, and $+5$ vanadium forms the acid HVO_3.)

The transition elements can have almost any oxidation state from 2 to the maximum for their group; thus chromium shows oxidation numbers of 2, 3, and 6; manganese, 2, 3, 4, 6, and 7. Manganese can also have an oxidation number of 1 in certain complex salts.

The metals and pseudo metals of the B subgroups that show more than one oxidation state behave differently. Here, only one electron shell is incomplete and available for chemical reactions, and this is the outermost shell. The electronic structure of tin, with atomic number 50, is (50) 2. 8. 18. 18. 4. The electrons in the fifth (outmost) shell are grouped with two in $5s$ and two in $5p$ levels. The two $5p$ electrons are more easily removed than the $5s$ electrons, so that tin can be oxidized by medium strength oxidizing agents to dipositive tin, for example Sn^{++}, $SnO_2^{=}$. However, stronger oxidation removes the $5s$ electrons also. Since these two electrons have very nearly equal potential energies, when one is removed or shared, the other will be removed or shared too; we cannot have an intermediate oxidation number of 3, only 2 and 4. Likewise, element 51, antimony, can have oxidation numbers of 3 and 5 but not 4; again, the two $5s$ electrons can either be left undisturbed, giving Sb^{+++}, or removed (or shared) together, giving $+5$ antimony. The pair of s electrons in these atoms has been called the *inert pair* by Sidgwick. Multiple oxidation states in these B-subgroup elements arise through the reluctance of these two s electrons to enter into reaction, and the oxidation numbers found are the maximum for the group and a value two units less.

Like many of the rules of chemistry, the rule just stated has its exceptions. Compounds are known, such as BiO_2, SbO_2, $(NH_4)_2SbBr_6$, $GaCl_2$, $InCl_2$, and possibly $CdCl$, in which the oxidation state of the metal appears to be irregular. Many of these irregularities vanish, however, when the magnetic susceptibilities of these compounds are considered. Sb^{+4} or Ga^{+2} would contain an odd number of electrons and would have to be paramagnetic, yet $(NH_4)_2$-$SbBr_6$, $GaCl_2$, $InCl_2$, and $CdCl$ have been shown to be diamagnetic.[3] In these substances the metal presumably exists in two different oxidation states, as in Pb_2O_3, for example, where one lead atom is $+2$ and the other $+4$. Nevertheless, there are a few genuine exceptions to the "inert pair" rule, for example BiO_2 and AsS.

If we look into the effect of atomic weight on the ease of oxidation within a given group, we again find a difference between the A subgroups (the transition elements) and the B subgroups. As the atomic weight increases in an A subgroup, the *higher* oxidation states become more stable. Thus Ti^{+4} is rather easily reduced to Ti^{+3}, but Zr^{+3}, Hf^{+3}, and Th^{+3} are unknown; Cr^{+6} is more easily reduced than Mo^{+6} (see Experiment 36); Mn^{+7} is powerfully oxidizing but Re^{+7} is not. In the B subgroups, on the other hand, with increasing atomic weight the *lower* oxidation states become more stable. Sn^{+2} is easily oxidized to Sn^{+4}, and compounds of tetrapositive tin are very stable, whereas compounds of tetrapositive lead are unstable and are powerful oxidizing agents (Experiments 8, 19, and 33). In Group $3B$, the only element that can readily be reduced from the $+3$ state to $+1$ is the heaviest, thallium.

The value of an oxidation-reduction potential depends on several factors, including ionization potentials, hydration energies, and nature of combination, so that the generalizations of the preceding paragraph should not be taken too rigidly. For example, in Group $6A$, $+6$ chromium exists in acid solution as $Cr_2O_7^=$, and $+6$ molybdenum and tungsten as similar anions; but $+6$ uranium exists as a cation, probably UO_2^{++}. Thus it is not surprising to find $+6$ uranium somewhat out of line, being more easily reduced (to $+3$) than tungsten, though less easily than chromium. However, the recent work of Glen T. Seaborg and others suggests

[3] See P. W. Selwood, *Magnetochemistry*. New York: Interscience Publishers, 1943, pages 139–141.

that uranium is not properly a Group 6 element at all, but a member of a rare-earth series starting with actinium.[4]

Disregarding the exceptions, which are actually very few, we can summarize the differences between A and B subgroups in the following way:

TABLE 7

OXIDATION STATES IN A AND B SUBGROUPS

A Subgroups	B Subgroups
	(Excluding Cu, Ag, Au and Br, I)
One element can have many oxidation states.	One element has only two positive oxidation states.
Oxidation numbers of an element may differ by 1 unit.	Oxidation numbers of an element differ by 2 units.
Ease of oxidation increases with increasing atomic weight.	Ease of oxidation decreases with increasing atomic weight.

In the nonmetals, such as N, P, S, and Cl, several oxidation states are known, but these generally arise through varying degrees of coordination. Thus in the ion $ClO_3{}^-$ the chlorine can accept a fourth oxygen atom by coordination, using a pair of its own electrons to form a coordinate link, yielding $ClO_4{}^-$. Here the oxidation numbers always change by two units at a time. Chlorine is known in oxidation states -1, $+1$, $+3$, $+5$, and $+7$, but not in intermediate states except in a few "odd molecules," such as ClO_2, which contain an odd number of electrons. In the halogens, the higher oxidation states become more stable with increasing atomic weight, except that the perbromate ion does not exist.

OXIDIZING AGENTS USED IN PREPARATIVE INORGANIC CHEMISTRY

Air. Air is of course the cheapest oxidizing agent, to be employed whenever possible. The oxidation-reduction potential of air is only 0.01 volt less negative than that of pure oxygen at the same pressure, so there is seldom any advantage in using pure oxygen, except that it reacts

[4] For full experimental data on oxidation-reduction potentials of different systems the reader is referred to W. M. Latimer, *Oxidation Potentials.* New York: Prentice-Hall, Inc., 1938.

faster than air. Preparations in this manual in which air
is used as the oxidizing agent, either alone or in conjunction
with a faster oxidizing agent such as chlorate, are numbers
10, 11, 35, 36, and 38.

Very often a catalyst is used in oxidations with air, as for
example in Experiment 10 or in the industrial oxidation of
SO_2 to SO_3, of NH_3 to NO, of HCl gas to Cl_2, and of
chromite mineral to $CaCrO_4$ (where $CaCO_3$ seems to act as
a catalyst).[5]

It was mentioned above that air is often a more effective
oxidizer in an alkaline medium than in an acid medium.
This statement is true of reactions in which a metal is
converted from a low oxidation state to a higher oxidation
state. In the higher oxidation state the oxide is more
strongly acid, and the alkali, by combining with the acidic
oxide, helps the reaction along. "Alkaline oxidation" by
air is a very common type of reaction, as the following few
examples will show:

$$3O_2 + 4Cr(OH)_3 + 8OH^- \rightarrow 4CrO_4^= + 10H_2O$$
$$O_2 + 4VO^{++} + 12OH^- \rightarrow 4VO_3^- + 6H_2O$$
$$O_2 + 2Bi(OH)_3 + 2OH^- \rightarrow 2BiO_3^- + 4H_2O$$
$$O_2 + 2SbO_3^= \rightarrow 2SbO_4^=$$

In the first three, hydroxyl ion is written as one of the
reactants and it is obvious that alkali will encourage the
reaction. In the fourth example, antimonic acid, H_3SbO_4,
is a stronger acid than antimonous (see Chapter IV), and
H_3SbO_3 is so weak that if the solution is *not* made strongly
alkaline, there will hardly be any $SbO_3^=$ at all.

"Alkaline oxidations" can be carried out in fused alkali
or in aqueous solution. The reactions in fused alkali are of
course faster.

It might be noted that in acid solution, oxygen reacts
rapidly only by the reaction: $O_2 + 2H^+ + 2e \rightarrow H_2O_2$, for
which $E^0 = -0.68$ volt. Thus an acidified solution of
potassium iodide is oxidized rapidly to iodine whereas an

[5] See H. A. Doerner, *Chem. and Met.*, **47** (1940), 688; also Experiment 35.

acidified solution of potassium bromide is not oxidized ($2Br^- \to Br_2 + 2e$, $E^0 = -1.07$ volt).

Hydrogen peroxide, peroxides, peroxy-acids, ozone. These are powerful oxidizing agents used for special tasks. Thus tripositive chromium is quickly oxidized to chromate in alkaline solution by hydrogen peroxide. Sodium peroxide combines alkaline character with its oxidizing power, and if chromite mineral is fused with sodium peroxide the chromium is quickly and completely converted to chromate. This is too expensive a process to be much used for preparative purposes, but for quantitative analysis it is ideal. Peroxy-acids, such as peroxysulfuric acid, are useful where a very powerful oxidizer is required, as in the preparation of dipositive silver salts (see above). An example of the use of 30% hydrogen peroxide in acid solution is given in this manual (Experiment 37; preparation of H_2SeO_4).

Ozone is seldom used as it is difficult to prepare in quantity, but it is a neat and powerful reagent, converting N_2O_4 quantitatively to N_2O_5, for example.

Hypochlorites, hypochlorous acid. A solution of sodium or calcium hypochlorite is a more powerful oxidizing agent than oxygen. Hypochlorite solutions are alkaline, since hypochlorous acid is very weak. Hypochlorite is, therefore, a reagent for alkaline oxidations. An example of its use is given in Experiment 33, the preparation of lead dioxide, where the main reaction is: $PbO_2^= + OCl^- \to PbO_3^= + Cl^-$. Alkali facilitates this reaction since plumbic acid is stronger than plumbous.

Hypochlorous acid is also a powerful oxidizing agent but it is not so commonly used in preparative inorganic chemistry as are hypochlorites.

Nitric acid. Hot concentrated nitric acid is a very powerful reagent, and is especially useful for making the higher oxides and oxyacids of the nonmetals:

$$I_2 + 10HNO_3 \to 2HIO_3 + 10NO_2 + 4H_2O$$
$$P + 5HNO_3 \to H_3PO_4 + 5NO_2 + H_2O$$
$$Se + 4HNO_3 \to H_2SeO_3 + 4NO_2 + H_2O$$
$$2H_2O + As_2O_3 + 2HNO_3 \to 2H_3AsO_4 + NO + NO_2$$

The last two reactions are performed in Experiments 37 and 34, respectively.

REDUCING AGENTS USED IN PREPARATIVE INORGANIC CHEMISTRY

Carbon and hydrogen. Carbon is by far the most important reducing agent, being used in the production of most metals from their ores. The active reducing agent is actually carbon monoxide, which is produced intermediately. This, being a gas, can permeate the granules of the oxide or other material being reduced, whereas the carbon can touch these granules at only a few points. Examples of the use of carbon as a reducing agent are given in Experiments 18, 42, and 43. Hydrogen is a more expensive reagent than carbon or carbon monoxide, but is preferred in reducing metal oxides where a metal of high purity, free from dissolved carbon or carbides, is required. Thus iron powder for powder metallurgy is made by reducing ferric oxide with hydrogen. The affinity of the metals tungsten and molybdenum for carbon is so great that their oxides must be reduced with hydrogen to get the metals; reduction with carbon gives the carbides.

Carbon and carbon monoxide are not satisfactory where chlorides or other halides are to be reduced, as in the preparation of anhydrous $TiCl_3$, Experiment 18; hydrogen is necessary for these reductions.

Metals. Metals, particularly the more active metals such as zinc, are frequently used in acid or alkaline solutions. Zinc is used in the manufacture of $Na_2S_2O_4$, sodium hydrosulfite, which is an extremely powerful reducing agent used in the dyestuffs industry. Experiment 45 in this manual illustrates the use of zinc in preparing lower salts of the transition metals. Aluminum is an important reducing agent at high temperatures; in the Goldschmidt or "thermite" process, the oxides of iron, chromium, or manganese are mixed with aluminum powder, and the reaction is started by burning magnesium. Intense heat is developed and the oxides are reduced to the metals. (See

Experiment 47.) Most of the transition metals can be produced in this way, and so can silicon and boron, though in an impure condition. Magnesium is being used to reduce the chlorides of zirconium and titanium to the metals at a high temperature.[6]

Sulfurous acid. This is a rather mild reducing agent suitable for such reductions as $VO_3^- \rightarrow VO^{++}$, where a more powerful reducer would take the vanadium down to the $+3$ or $+2$ state. It has the advantage that it is unstable, so that excess sulfurous acid can be boiled away. Reductions using sulfurous acid are illustrated by Experiments 6, 44, and 46.

[6] See W. H. Waggaman and E. A. Gee, *Chem. and Eng. News*, **26** (1948) 377.

CHAPTER VII

Electrolytic Preparations[1]

In Chapter VI we defined oxidation as the loss of electrons and reduction as the gain of electrons, and we showed that oxidation-reduction reactions that involve ions can generally be made to produce an electric current. Chemical energy is thereby transformed into electrical energy, and the electromotive force of the cell is a measure of the free energy of the reaction. Conversely, we can make an electric current produce a chemical reaction. If a current is passed through an electrolyte—a conducting solution or molten salt—oxidation takes place at the anode, where electrons are withdrawn from the solution; and reduction takes place simultaneously at the cathode, where the electrons enter.

Some reactions which are possible in no other way can be brought about by an electric current. For example, fluorine is the most powerful oxidizing agent known, and the only way of liberating fluorine from fluorides or hydrofluoric acid is by means of an electric current. Other strong oxidizing agents, such as cobaltic sulfate, are most readily prepared by electrolysis; and powerful reducing agents, such as the alkali metals, which are very difficult to produce by chemical means, are easily liberated at the cathode in electrolysis. The oxidizing or reducing action can be made as powerful as desired, simply by raising the potential (or voltage) applied to the electrodes.

Electrolytic methods have the advantage of power and general application; they also have the advantage that they yield very pure products. Many metals, such as copper,

[1] A very complete review of electrolytic preparations, both organic and inorganic, is to be found in S. Glasstone and A. Hickling, *Electrolytic Oxidation and Reduction*. London: Chapman & Hall, 1935.

zinc, lead, and aluminum, are refined electrolytically. If we want to prepare a solution of chromous chloride, we can reduce a chromic chloride solution by zinc and hydrochloric acid, as in Experiment 45, but the solution obtained contains a good deal of zinc chloride as well as the desired chromous chloride, and the separation of the desired product from the by-product is not easy. But if we reduce a chromic chloride solution electrolytically, the product is a pure solution of chromous chloride with no by-products.

Electrolytic methods have two disadvantages. First, they often require complicated and expensive equipment. Measures must usually be taken to keep the products of reduction at the cathode from being reoxidized at the anode, or vice versa; moreover, the electrodes must sometimes be made of expensive materials such as platinum or mercury. Second, the progress of an electrolytic reaction depends on the quantity of electricity passed; and unless very large currents are used, it takes a long time to pass enough electricity.

For convenience we can divide electrolytic processes into those carried out in fused baths and those in aqueous solutions. No examples of the electrolysis of fused salts are given in this manual,[2] but they are very important in industry; sodium, potassium, calcium, magnesium, and aluminum are all made by the electrolysis of molten salts, with chlorine appearing as a by-product in all the above except aluminum. The only chemical difficulty in these processes is to obtain a melt which is a good conductor and has as low a melting point as possible. The main difficulty is in the design of equipment to withstand the high temperatures and the vigorous chemical action of the electrolyte and products at these temperatures.

Perhaps we should include the production of fluorine, which has recently reached commercial proportions, in the

---

[2] The best account of the electrolysis of fused salts is P. Drossbach's *Elektrolyse geschmolzener Salze*. Berlin: Springer, 1938. Reprinted by Edwards Bros., Ann Arbor, 1943.

category of electrolysis of fused salts. The electrolyte is a liquid mixture of potassium acid fluoride and anhydrous hydrofluoric acid, usually in the ratio 1 formula weight of KHF_2 to 1 formula weight of HF, and the temperature is about 100°. Carbon anodes are used.[3]

The electrolysis of *aqueous solutions* is complicated by the fact that the ions of water, hydrogen and hydroxyl, are always present, and an electrical potential strong enough to perform the desired oxidation or reduction may also be strong enough to liberate oxygen or hydrogen from the water. Thus when an aqueous solution of sodium chloride is electrolyzed, sodium is not liberated at the cathode. Instead, the hydrogen ions of the water are reduced to hydrogen, and sodium hydroxide is produced around the cathode. Likewise, any attempt to produce fluorine by electrolyzing a solution of a fluoride in water would yield only oxygen at the anode, not fluorine.

From the table of oxidation-reduction potentials we might conclude that no metal above hydrogen in the electromotive series could ever be liberated by electrolysis from an acidified aqueous solution, and that hydrogen would always be liberated first. Yet it is possible to plate out metals like lead, tin, nickel, chromium, and even zinc from acid solutions. It is also possible to reduce chromic salts quantitatively to chromous salts at a cathode in acid solution, in spite of the fact that the standard potential of the half reaction $Cr^{++} \rightarrow Cr^{+++} + e$ is $+0.4$ volt (that is, chromous ions should spontaneously reduce hydrogen ions to hydrogen gas). Similarly, it is possible to oxidize sulfate ions to persulfate in acid solutions, despite the fact that the standard potential of $2SO_4^= \rightarrow S_2O_8^= + 2e$ is -2.05 volt, or 0.82 volt more oxidizing than the half reaction $2H_2O \rightarrow 4H^+ + O_2 + 4e$. Such reactions are possible because the discharge of hydrogen and oxygen can be hindered by using the effect known as overvoltage.

[3] See the various articles in the Fluorine Symposium in *Industrial and Engineering Chemistry*, **39** (1947), 244–271.

Overvoltage. If a 1-molar solution of copper sulfate is electrolyzed, copper will start to plate out on the cathode as soon as the latter has reached a potential of +0.34 volt. This is the standard potential for the half reaction $Cu^{++} + 2e \rightarrow Cu$ and is equal and opposite to the standard potential for $Cu \rightarrow Cu^{++} + 2e$, as defined in Chapter VI. If the cathode is made more negative than +0.34 volt (referred

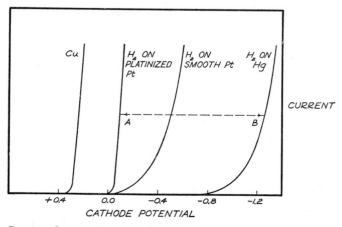

Fig. 8. Current-voltage curves for the discharge of hydrogen and copper.

to the standard hydrogen electrode), the current, which is proportional to the rate of deposition of copper, rises very steeply indeed and is limited only by the electrical resistance of the solution.

If, however, a dilute acid is electrolyzed so that hydrogen is given off at the cathode, the cathode must usually be made more negative than the standard potential for $2H^+ + 2e \rightarrow H_2$, which is ±0.00 volt, before the evolution of hydrogen is appreciable. As the cathode is made more negative, the current increases, though not so rapidly with increasing voltage as is the case with copper, and it bears an exponential relation to the voltage. The difference in behavior is shown in Fig. 8. The voltage required to discharge hydrogen is different with different cathode materials, and only on a highly catalytic cathode surface, such as platinized platinum, does the discharge current of hydrogen resemble that of copper or any other metal. For other cathodes an excess of negative potential, represented by the line AB, is necessary. This excess, called the overvoltage, depends primarily on the nature of the cathode metal. In general, the softer the metal and the poorer its catalytic powers, the greater the overvoltage; thus it is greatest for mercury. Overvoltage increases with current density and decreases with rising temperature. Its exact cause is so far unknown, but it is due to the slowness of one of the chemical processes involved in the production of hydrogen molecules from hydrogen ions and electrons.[4] Oxygen shows overvoltage in the same way as hydrogen, but in the deposition of metals no overvoltage can be detected except in a very few cases.

If we want to bring about a difficult oxidation or reduction, requiring a high potential at the anode or the cathode, we must take steps to make the overvoltage as high as possible and so slow down the discharge of oxygen or hydrogen. We can do this by choosing the appropriate material for the electrode and by using a high current density and a low temperature. The effect of the electrode material is seen in Table 8. The overvoltages there quoted refer to room temperature and a current density of about 10^{-3} amp/cm². Since overvoltage is affected greatly by the condition of the electrode surface, the values are approximate only.

For example, in the anodic oxidation of sulfates to peroxysulfates (Experiment 48), platinum, a metal with a high oxygen overvoltage, is used as the anode, the anode is made very small and therefore the current density is very high, and the temperature is kept low. In this way the evolution

[4] The current follows the same law as the speed of a chemical reaction: that is,

$$\text{Current} = k.e^{-E/RT}$$

where k is a constant and E is an activation energy, equal to $E_0 - \alpha VF$, where E_0 depends on the cathode; V is the overvoltage, and α is approximately 0.5 for most metals; F is the faraday.

of oxygen at the anode is not prevented, but it is slowed down enough that peroxydisulfate is formed as well as oxygen. (If the anode in this experiment is made very much larger than specified, the yield of peroxysulfate will be negligible.) The oxidation of chlorate ion to perchlorate ion is not so difficult as the oxidation of sulfate to peroxysulfate, but is difficult enough that an anode of platinum is necessary (Experiment 50). In commercial practice, cooled platinum-plated copper anodes are used.

TABLE 8

Overvoltages for Hydrogen and Oxygen

Electrode	Hydrogen overvoltage	Oxygen overvoltage
Platinized platinum...................	0.00	0.25
Iron..............................	0.08	0.25
Smooth platinum.....................	0.09	0.45
Nickel.............................	0.2	0.06
Copper............................	0.2	....
Tin................................	0.5	....
Lead..............................	0.6	0.3
Zinc...............................	0.7	....
Mercury...........................	0.8	....

In the reduction of titanic chloride to titanous chloride (Experiment 51), a cathode of lead is used, on account of the high overvoltage of hydrogen on lead. Where a more powerful reducing action is required, the cathode can be of amalgamated lead or mercury. A mercury cathode is used in the Castner-Kellner cell for manufacturing sodium hydroxide; brine (sodium chloride solution) is electrolyzed, and sodium amalgam is formed. Then the latter is run into a chamber containing water, where it reacts to form pure sodium hydroxide. It is possible to liberate metallic sodium in the electrolysis of brine with a mercury cathode, first, because the sodium dissolves in the mercury and its activity is thereby greatly lowered, and second, because the very high overvoltage of hydrogen on mercury represses the liberation of hydrogen.

We can see from the table of overvoltages how it is possible, for example, to plate out metallic zinc from an acid electrolyte, as is done in the manufacture of "electrolytic zinc," because zinc happens to have a very high overvoltage for hydrogen, about as high as the standard potential of the zinc electrode itself.

Cell design for aqueous solutions. The experiments in this text show some of the points of the design of electrolytic cells for preparative purposes. As a rule the anode and cathode compartments must be kept separate by means of a porous pot or diaphragm, which should be so designed as not to cause undue electrical resistance. Sometimes a diaphragm is unnecessary, as in the preparation of potassium peroxydisulfate, where there is little opportunity for the peroxydisulfate to be reduced at the cathode, because it is sparingly soluble and falls to the bottom of the electrolysis vessel. In the preparation of perchlorate no diaphragm is used, the reduction of the product at the cathode being inhibited by the addition of sodium chromate. Adding sodium chromate is a common practice; it seems that the chromate is partially reduced at the cathode, with the formation of a film of chromic chromate that surrounds the cathode and acts as a diaphragm to prevent the diffusion of perchlorate to the cathode surface.

Thus in the electrolysis of sodium or potassium chloride solution to produce chlorate (Experiment 49), not only is no diaphragm used, but the electrodes are so arranged as to give the maximum possible mixing between the solution at the anode and the solution at the cathode. This arrangement is adopted because the product desired is not directly produced by the electrolysis but results from the chlorine liberated at the anode reacting with the potassium hydroxide liberated at the cathode. However, we still have to guard against reduction of chlorate at the cathode, and for this reason chromate is added.

The same cell that is used to produce chlorate could also be used to produce hypochlorite, but in this case the temperature must be kept low and the solution must be alkaline. Both hypochlorites and chlorates are produced commercially by the electrolysis of brine.

A frequent difficulty in large-scale electrolytic preparations is to keep the solution cool, since the resistance of the solution to the electric current causes considerable heat to be developed. Cooling coils must be placed in the cells, and in some cases hollow electrodes are used through which cooling water circulates.

Current efficiency. From the equation of the oxidation or reduction process one can calculate the maximum yield of product to be expected from a given quantity of electricity. Thus in the reduction

$$TiO^{++} + 2H^+ + e \rightarrow Ti^{+++} + H_2O$$

a mole of titanium salt should be reduced by 1 faraday of electricity, that is, by 96,500 coulombs. A coulomb of electricity is the quantity passing when 1 amp flows for 1 second, so that a faraday is the amount of electricity passed when a current of 1 amp flows for 96,500 seconds, or 10 amperes for 9,650 seconds, and so on. In the oxidation

$$ClO_3^- + H_2O \rightarrow ClO_4^- + 2H^+ + 2e$$

2 faradays of electricity are needed to oxidize 1 mole of chlorate. In practice, the yield of product is often less than the maximum, owing to side reactions such as the evolution of oxygen or hydrogen or the reduction or oxidation of some of the product. In electrolytic preparations a record should always be kept of the current and the time for which it is passed, so that the number of coulombs passed can be calculated, and from it the maximum yield of product. The ratio of the actual yield obtained to the maximum yield is known as the *current efficiency*. It should always be reported when an electrolytic preparation has been performed.

Compounds prepared by electrolytic oxidation or reduction in aqueous solutions. Among the inorganic compounds most advantageously prepared by electrolytic oxidation are hypochlorites, chlorates and perchlorates, peroxysulfates (and from them, hydrogen peroxide), other peroxyacids and their salts, permanganates, dichromates (from chromic salt solutions left after organic compounds have been oxidized by chromic acid), ferricyanides, and highly oxidized unstable compounds such as cobaltic sulfate and ceric perchlorate. Electrolytic reduction is used to prepare hydroxylamine, titanous salts, and other salts of the transition elements in low oxidation states. Both electrolytic oxidation and reduction can be used in preparative organic chemistry.

THE PREPARATIONS

1. Pure Sodium Chloride from Common Salt

Dissolve 50 grams of common salt in 150 ml of hot water. Cool, filter, and test small portions of the solution qualitatively for sulfate, calcium, and magnesium. To test for sulfate, add barium chloride and dilute hydrochloric acid; for calcium, add ammonium oxalate; for magnesium, add a few drops of a dilute solution of the dye paranitrobenzene-azo-resorcinol, followed by 2N sodium hydroxide. In the last test, magnesium gives magnesium

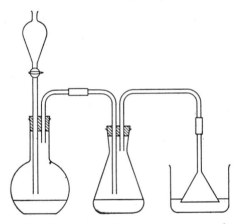

Fig. 9. Pure sodium chloride from common salt.

hydroxide colored blue by the dye; the blue is distinct from the purple color the dye itself gives with sodium hydroxide.

Place the remaining solution in an Erlenmeyer flask and pass over it a slow stream of hydrogen chloride gas, generated by dropping concentrated sulfuric acid into concentrated hydrochloric acid. To prevent the hydrogen chloride gas from passing out into the room, it is absorbed in sodium hydroxide solution by use of the funnel arrangement shown in Fig. 9. *Note:* (a) The gas is passed over the salt solution and not through it. (b) The funnel dips only a millimeter or so below the surface of the sodium hydroxide. The reasons for these arrangements should be clear.

Pure sodium chloride precipitates from the solution, the impurities remaining in solution.   Note the shape of the crystals as they form.   When a substantial precipitate has formed, filter it on the Büchner funnel, rinse with a very little cold concentrated hydrochloric acid, then dry in an evaporating dish on the steam bath. Use a glass spatula, not steel, for the manipulations.

Dissolve a gram or so of product in 15 ml of distilled water and test this solution as before for sulfate, calcium, and magnesium.   It is not necessary to report the yield in this preparation, but turn in your product.

QUESTIONS

1. Why does sodium chloride precipitate, whereas the impurities do not?

2. Why not purify the sodium chloride by simply recrystallizing it from hot water?

3. Why does concentrated sulfuric acid displace hydrogen chloride from its solution in water?   Account for the lack of any considerable evolution of heat when the sulfuric acid is added to the hydrochloric acid solution.

2. Sodium Perchlorate

This preparation illustrates the production of a very soluble salt from an acid and a base.   The aim is to get a good yield of a neutral product.   The water of crystallization of the salt will also be determined.

Weigh out 0.6 mole of sodium hydroxide, dissolve in about 60 ml of distilled water, and make the volume of the solution up to 100 ml in graduated cylinder.   At the same time, procure some 60 per cent perchloric acid and determine the volume of this acid that reacts with unit volume of sodium hydroxide by taking a small volume of sodium hydroxide (say 2 ml measured by a pipette) and making up to 100 ml in a volumetric flask; transfer to a clean, dry flask, rinse the volumetric flask and pipette, and dilute the perchloric acid in exactly the same manner.   Fill a burette with the diluted perchloric acid and titrate 25-ml portions of the diluted sodium hydroxide.   Since both the acid and the base are strong, almost any indicator will be satisfactory. When you have two titrations that agree to about 0.5 per cent, pour the remaining 98 ml of 6-molar sodium hydroxide into a beaker and add to it the calculated volume of 60 per cent per-chloric acid required for exact neutralization. Check the neutrality of the solution with litmus, adding a drop or two more acid or base if necessary.

The solution after mixing will be hot from the heat of neutralization. Evaporate it on the steam bath to about 120 ml; filter it further, while hot, from any sediment; evaporate to about 80 ml, and cool the filtrate to room temperature; finally cool in ice and filter out the crystals on a small Büchner funnel. Recrystallize from a minimum volume of hot water, again cooling in ice to get the crystals. Suck them as dry as possible and bottle them. Dissolve a small amount of the salt in water and test for neutrality with methyl red, and for chloride ion with silver nitrate.

To determine the water of crystallization, a sample free from adherent moisture must be obtained. Take about half of your product and dry it in the oven at 120° for about an hour; it falls into a powder of anhydrous salt. Put this salt into a wide-mouth screw-cap bottle. Weigh a small stoppered weighing bottle accurately and put into the bottle about a gram of damp sodium per-chlorate crystals. Then put the weighing bottle, without its stopper, upright into the wide-mouth bottle along with the anhydrous salt; close the wide-mouth bottle, which acts as a small desiccator, and leave it in your desk for a few days. During this time the salt hydrate and anhydrous salt come to equilibrium. The two-phase system in the bottom of the large bottle, hydrate plus anhydrous salt, has one vapor pressure; the system hydrate plus saturated solution in the weighing bottle has another, higher vapor pressure. Water vapor, therefore, distills from the wet crystals to the anhydrous salt until there is no more solution left, but when distillation is complete, the hydrate loses no more water. This method is standard for preparing dry specimens of salt hydrates without running any risk of dehydrating them (see Chapter III).

When the hydrate is dry, remove the weighing bottle, stopper it immediately, clean the outside, and weigh accurately. Put it in the oven at 120°, with the stopper off, for about two hours; remove stopper, cool to room temperature, and weigh again. From your weighings calculate the percentage of water in sodium perchlorate hydrate and the number of molecules of water of crystallization of the salt.

QUESTIONS

1. What was the flocculent precipitate you probably observed after the sodium hydroxide and perchloric acid were mixed, and how did it get there?

2. Compare the solubilities of sodium perchlorate and potassium perchlorate.

3. Anhydrous Magnesium Chloride

The production of anhydrous magnesium chloride from the hydrate is of great industrial importance, since nearly all metallic magnesium is made from the melted anhydrous chloride by electrolysis. It is an operation of considerable difficulty and illustrates both the ease of hydrolysis and the great energy of hydration of this salt.

Magnesium chloride forms four hydrates, $MgCl_2 \cdot H_2O$, $MgCl_2 \cdot 2H_2O$, $MgCl_2 \cdot 4H_2O$, and $MgCl_2 \cdot 6H_2O$, of which the last is the one obtained from aqueous solutions at ordinary temperatures. When heated, the hexahydrate loses water in steps, corresponding to formation of the next lowest hydrate, as is illustrated in the vapor-pressure graph, Fig. 10. In the first two dehydration steps, the water vapor can be driven off in a stream of air without danger of hydrolysis. The last two molecules of water of hydration must be removed by heating in hydrogen chloride gas. During the removal of water, the salt must not melt in its water of crystallization; otherwise it will cake, and further dehydration will be very difficult.

Take 5 grams of $MgCl_2 \cdot 6H_2O$ crystals, which must be as dry as possible, and place in a wide-mouth 250-ml extraction flask. This flask is fitted with a cork with two holes, one 10 mm in diameter, the other narrower and carrying a glass tube that reaches nearly to the bottom of the flask. Clamp the flask in a beaker of cottonseed oil (no larger than necessary) in which is a thermometer reading to 300°C. Pass in air through the glass tube from the compressed-air line, first passing the air through a sulfuric acid bubbler of the spiral type. A fast rate of bubbling should be maintained. Heat the oil bath to 110°; then raise the temperature to 120° over a period of half an hour, slowly, since there is danger of the salt melting above 110° if it is heated too fast.   Above 120°, if no more water vapor is coming off (test by inserting a small test tube of cold water loosely into the outlet hole of the cork), heat rapidly to 150°; again heat slowly to 160°. Above this temperature, hydrogen chloride must be substituted for the air stream.   Use as a generator a 1-liter Florence flask containing about 100 grams of common salt, and let concentrated sulfuric acid drip onto this from a separatory funnel.   Pass the hydrogen chloride through the sulfuric acid bubbler as you did

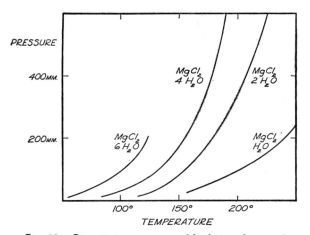

Fig. 10.   Dissociation pressures of hydrates of magnesium chloride.   (Data of Smith and Veazey, U.S. Patent 1,835,818; 1929.)

the compressed air.   *This part of the heating must be done in the hood,* although if desired, the hydrogen chloride leaving the flask with the magnesium chloride in it can be led away by a wide tube inserted in the cork (a tube narrower than 8 mm internally will condense moisture and let it drip back on the salt) and absorbed in sodium hydroxide, with the usual precautions to prevent a suck back (see Experiment 1).   Continue heating up to 260–270°, heating slowly around 200° to avoid melting.   Stop heating only when no more moisture seems to be coming off. The entire heating period is about three hours.

This product should be a white or slightly gray porous mass. It is now melted at a red heat in a weighed Pyrex test tube (25 × 200 mm) under a stream of hydrogen chloride gas.   A little more water may be released during melting.   The fused salt attacks the glass, but it should yield a fairly clear melt that solidifies to a glassy solid. A really clear melt cannot be obtained unless a quartz or metal tube is used. Rotate the tube during solidification. Show your solidified salt to the instructor but do not hand it in. Weigh the test tube and salt and record the yield, comparing it with the theoretical.

Chip a piece of anhydrous salt out of the test tube, put it in a dry tube, and add a little water. Note the considerable heating that takes place.

While this experiment is going on, heat a little magnesium chloride hexahydrate in a porcelain crucible over a Bunsen flame until all the water is given off. Heat the solid residue to redness and see if it can be melted. Cool and take up in water. Compare this residue with the anhydrous magnesium chloride that you produced in the manner described above.

QUESTIONS

1. Compare the hydration and hydrolysis of magnesium chloride with that of (a) sodium chloride, (b) barium chloride. Account for the differences in terms of ionic radius and charge.

2. Describe two reactions that will produce anhydrous magnesium chloride directly.

4. Double Salts

Double salts are formed when two simple salts crystallize together in definite, simple molecular proportions. They have their own crystal form, which need not be the same as that of either of their component salts. They are a phenomenon of the solid state; in solution they are decomposed completely, or nearly so, into the ions of their component salts. In this respect double salts are distinguished from complex salts, which give complex ions of their own in solution. Double salts are extremely numerous. Two examples will be prepared.

(A) $CuSO_4 \cdot (NH_4)_2SO_4 \cdot 6H_2O$. Dissolve 0.1 mole of copper sulfate pentahydrate and 0.1 mole of ammonium sulfate in 40 ml of hot water. Cool slowly. When the solution is cold, filter off the crystals on a Büchner funnel and dry them on filter paper in the air. Weigh, and record the yield. Examine them to see if they are homogeneous. Compare their appearance and behavior in solution with that of the complex salt cupric tetrammine sulfate, $Cu(NH_3)_4SO_4 \cdot H_2O$, which may be obtained from the side shelf or prepared as a separate exercise (Experiment 5).

This salt will separate in large well-formed crystals if a cold saturated solution is left to evaporate slowly in the air. The crystals belong to the monoclinic system.

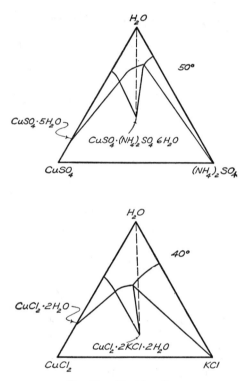

Fig. 11. Double salts.

(B) $CuCl_2 \cdot 2KCl \cdot 2H_2O$. Dissolve 0.25 mole of cupric chloride hydrate and 0.30 mole of potassium chloride in 40 ml of hot water, and cool slowly. When the solution is cold, filter it on a Büchner funnel and dry the crystals as well as possible with filter paper. The crystals are efflorescent and should not stand in the air long; otherwise they lose water and become brown. When dry but completely hydrated, they are green-blue in color. They are dried without losing their water of hydration by putting them in a desiccator over wet calcium nitrate, which gives a constant relative humidity of 51 per cent at 25°C.

Dissolve about 5 grams of the salt in just enough warm water (about 50°C) to bring about solution; then cool until the first crystals appear. Filter these crystals under suction, using a very small filter (a filter made by putting a small plug of glass wool in the neck of a glass filter funnel, and then covering the glass wool with a slight coating of asbestos fibers, is satisfactory). Alternatively, pour off the mother liquor, quickly transfer the mass of moist crystals to a small centrifuge tube packed with glass wool, and centrifuge, using a second packed tube for balancing. Note the appearance of the crystals. What are they? Can this double salt be purified by direct recrystallization?

Prepare 10 to 15 ml of dilute solutions of each of these double salts and a similar solution of cupric sulfate. Compare their colors and explain.

QUESTIONS

1. Make a list of half a dozen double salts that are important in industry or in laboratory practice.

2. How is potassium chloride extracted from carnallite? How would you make a sample of carnallite in the laboratory?

Note: To show the difference in stability of the two double cupric salts prepared, the phase diagrams in Fig. 11 are included. The middle portions of the curves represent the range of solution compositions which are in equilibrium with the double salts. If we dissolve $CuSO_4 \cdot (NH_4)_2\text{-}$ $SO_4 \cdot 6H_2O$ in water, we get a solution represented by a point somewhere on the dotted line in the first diagram. If we evaporate this solution, the graph shows that we shall crystallize the double salt out again. From the second diagram we see that the solutions which deposit potassium cupric chloride all contain proportionately more cupric chloride than is present in the double salt. Therefore, when the double salt is dissolved in water and the water is evaporated, potassium chloride is the first salt to separate out.

As an optional exercise, draw a rough phase diagram for the system $KCl\text{-}MgCl_2\text{-}H_2O$.

5. Tetrammine Cupric Sulfate

When ammonia is added to a solution of a cupric salt, a light-blue precipitate of cupric hydroxide is first formed which dissolves in excess of ammonia to form a deep purplish-blue solution. The color is due to the complex ion $Cu(NH_3)_4^{++}$. The sulfate of this ion is easily obtained in solid form as the hydrate $Cu(NH_3)_4$-$SO_4\cdot H_2O$.

Dissolve 12.5 grams (0.05 mole) of powdered copper sulfate pentahydrate in a mixture of 20 ml of concentrated ammonia and 12 ml of water, and slowly add to the blue solution 20 ml of ethyl alcohol. Allow it to stand about an hour, finally cooling thoroughly, and filter the crystals on a Büchner funnel. Wash first with a mixture of equal volumes of alcohol and concentrated ammonia, then with alcohol, and finally with ether. Dry in a desiccator over freshly ignited quicklime. The final product must be dry and free from alcohol.

Compare this salt in appearance and properties with the double salt, $CuSO_4\cdot(NH_4)_2SO_4\cdot 6H_2O$, prepared in Experiment 4. Dissolve a little of each salt in water and compare the resulting solutions.

Another way to precipitate the complex salt from its aqueous solution is to pour the alcohol carefully over the top of the solution and set aside for a week. As the alcohol slowly diffuses into the aqueous solution, long needlelike crystals of the tetrammine cupric sulfate form at the boundary.

QUESTIONS

1. Name six other metallic cations that form complex ions with ammonia.

2. When this salt is dissolved in water, a slight precipitate appears. What is this precipitate, and why is it formed?

3. Why is the salt dried over quicklime instead of over calcium chloride?

4. What is the difference in constitution between tetrammine cupric sulfate and cupric ammonium sulfate?

6. Potassium Mercuriiodide and Cuprous Mercuriiodide

The element mercury is distinguished by the vast number of covalent compounds which it forms. Thus it is said that more metal-organic compounds of mercury are known than of all the other metals put together. However, mercury forms relatively few complex ions. Two salts of one of these, the ion $HgI_4^=$, are prepared in this exercise. The preparation of the potassium salt will illustrate the crystallization of a very soluble salt; moreover, potassium mercuriiodide is a useful reagent. The cuprous salt is extremely easy to prepare but is interesting for its occurrence in two crystalline forms having different colors, one red, the other black.

(A) *Potassium mercuriiodide.* First precipitate some mercuric iodide by mixing a solution of 13.5 grams (0.05 mole) of mercuric chloride in 150 ml of warm water with a solution of 16.6 grams (0.10 mole) of potassium iodide in 50 ml of water. Pour the potassium iodide into the mercuric chloride, stirring thoroughly. Filter off the red mercuric iodide, wash it with hot water, and suck it as dry as possible on a Büchner funnel, though do not let it dry completely. Stir it into a hot solution of 16.0 grams of potassium iodide in 10 ml of water. Heat the mixture on the steam bath for half an hour, stirring occasionally, to make sure the solution becomes saturated with mercuric iodide. Then centrifuge off the small excess of mercuric iodide, or filter it off if no centrifuge is available. Place the solution in a crystallizing dish in a vacuum desiccator over calcium chloride, and leave it for a few hours until nearly all the water has evaporated. If a crust of crystals forms over the surface of the solution and hinders evaporation, open the desiccator and break up the crust with a pointed glass rod; then close the desiccator again and re-evacuate.

When nearly all the water has evaporated and a mush of yellow crystals remains, scrape the mush of crystals out of the dish and smear it on a wad of several thicknesses of filter paper, which will absorb the mother liquor together with any impurities this solution may contain. Put the filter paper with the crystals on it back into the desiccator, evacuate it, and leave the paper until the crystals are quite dry. They should be large light-yellow crystals with no sign of any colorless potassium iodide crystals. The formula of the salt is $K_2HgI_4 \cdot 2H_2O$.

Another and neater way of separating the crystals from the adherent mother liquor is to pack two balanced 12-ml centrifuge tubes each half full with glass wool, distribute the crystal mush equally between the two tubes so that they remain balanced, and centrifuge for a few minutes (see Chapter III). This salt is used in preparing Nessler's solution, a sensitive reagent for ammonia, and is worth keeping. It may, however, be used for the preparation to follow.

(B) *Cuprous mercuriiodide.* Dissolve 0.015 mole of potassium mercuriiodide in 50 ml of water, or prepare a solution of potassium mercuriiodide as follows: Dissolve 4.1 grams of mercuric chloride in 40 ml of water; then add to this solution, slowly and with constant stirring, a solution of 12 grams of potassium iodide in 20 ml of water. Add just enough potassium iodide so that the precipitate of mercuric iodide first formed redissolves, but no more. Then stir in slowly a solution of 7.5 grams of copper sulfate pentahydrate in 45 ml of water, watching carefully what happens. When the copper sulfate is all added, pass a stream of sulfur dioxide (hood!). The sulfur dioxide is drawn from a cylinder or generated by dripping concentrated hydrochloric acid onto sodium bisulfite. When the solution continues to smell of sulfur dioxide, even after shaking and standing, filter off the red precipitate of cuprous mercuriiodide, wash with a little water, and dry at 110°.

To find the temperature of transition between red and black forms, put a little of the material into a small thin-walled glass tube as if you were going to determine a melting point, attach the tube to a thermometer with a rubber band, support in a beaker of water, and gradually heat, noting the temperature at which the salt changes color. Then allow it to cool gradually, again noting the temperature of the color change. Locate this temperature as accurately as you can. It should be 71°.

QUESTIONS

1. Does the salt K_2HgCl_4 exist? On the basis of the covalency rules, how would you expect it to compare in stability with K_2HgI_4?

2. What is the formula of the brown precipitate obtained when an alkaline solution of potassium mercuriiodide reacts with ammonia?

3. In Part B, if the potassium mercuriiodide and copper sulfate solutions are not too dilute, some red cuprous mercuriiodide appears even before the sulfur dioxide is passed. Account for this on the basis of oxidation-reduction potentials.

4. What is the effect of heat on solid K_2HgI_4? (Perform an experiment to help answer this question, if necessary.)

7. Potassium Fluotitanate

Potassium fluotitanate, K_2TiF_6, is a convenient source for the preparation of other titanium salts. It can easily be obtained pure because it is sparingly soluble (0.6 gram in 100 grams of water at 0°), and it is therefore used as a primary standard in oxidation-reduction titrations. Its existence and stability illustrate the power of the fluoride ion to form stable complex ions and to bring out the highest coordination number of an element.

Dissolve 5 grams of finely powdered titanium dioxide in 25 grams of concentrated aqueous hydrofluoric acid in a clean, shallow sheet-iron dish. Heat just to boiling, to dissolve as much titanium dioxide as possible; then add 10 grams of anhydrous potassium fluoride, or an equivalent amount of $KF \cdot 2H_2O$, dissolved in not more than 10 ml of water. Stir well with an iron file; then evaporate the solution quickly to dryness. Do not heat any more than is necessary. The hydrofluoric acid attacks the iron somewhat during the evaporation, but the iron will not contaminate the product.

Extract the mass in the dish with 200 to 250 ml of boiling water. The solution may now be transferred to a glass beaker, since most of the hydrofluoric acid has been driven off. Filter the hot solution and cool, finally cooling in ice. Potassium fluotitanate crystallizes as a fine white powder. Though already fairly pure, for analytical use it should be recrystallized once more.

Test a portion of the product for iron by heating it with concentrated sulfuric acid in a platinum crucible to drive off hydrofluoric acid; then cool, dilute with water, and add potassium thiocyanate solution. (A lead dish and 70 per cent sulfuric acid may be used instead of the platinum crucible.) There should not be more than a faint orange reaction to indicate the presence of ferric iron. With the recrystallized material there should be no reaction at all.

QUESTIONS

1. The solution obtained by extracting the solid in the dish contained iron. Why was it not colored?

2. Why was the salt heated with sulfuric acid to drive off hydrogen fluoride before testing for iron?

3. How would you prepare a standard solution of titanous sulfate from this product, for use in volumetric analysis?

4. What is meant by the term "coordination number"? On what does the coordination number of an element depend?

5. The salt K_2TiCl_6 is not nearly as stable as K_2TiF_6. How do you reconcile this fact with the covalency rules? (See Chapter V.)

8. Ammonium Chloroplumbate and Lead Tetrachloride

These compounds of tetrapositive lead correspond to the tin compounds prepared in Experiment 19. Compounds of tetrapositive lead are much less stable than compounds of tetrapositive tin, owing to the greater inertness of the so-called "inert pair of electrons" in the atom of lead (see Chapter VI); that is, +4 lead will gain two electrons very easily to form +2 lead. This property is very apparent in this experiment.

Suspend 5 grams of lead dioxide in 20 ml of ice-cold concentrated hydrochloric acid, cool in ice, and pass in chlorine slowly, shaking the solution occasionally until it is clear. This operation may take about two hours. A solid white residue remains at the bottom of the tube, but the supernatant liquid should be a clear yellow. Decant the solution, and into it stir 5 grams of solid ammonium chloride. Yellow crystals of ammonium chloroplumbate, $(NH_4)_2PbCl_6$, separate immediately. Filter them quickly and wash them with a little ice water and then with ice-cold alcohol. Dry them on a watch glass at room temperature. The salt may be left exposed to the air at room temperature for a few hours without appreciable decomposition, but it should be transferred to a tightly closed bottle for storage. The yield is about 60 per cent.

Lead tetrachloride. Place a gram or two of the salt in a dry test tube, cool in ice, and slowly add a few milliliters of ice-cold concentrated sulfuric acid. Lead tetrachloride separates as an oil. Note any other products.

Tests with ammonium chloroplumbate:

1. Dissolve a little of the salt in water and note whether any decomposition takes place.

2. Warm a little of the dry salt in a test tube. Also warm a little ammonium chlorostannate and note the contrast.

1. Name three of the more stable compounds of tetrapositive lead, and generalize, if you can, about the conditions required for the stability of tetrapositive lead compounds.

2. Which is more salt-like, $PbCl_2$ or $PbCl_4$?

9. Complex Iron Salts

(A) *Potassium ferric oxalate,* $K_3Fe(C_2O_4)_3 \cdot 3H_2O$. The metals of the iron group are noted for the variety of complex ions which they form, and the oxalate ion is a good complex former. The ferric oxalate complex ion is, accordingly, quite a stable one. The method to be described for preparing potassium ferric oxalate can be used for a number of other complex oxalate salts, such as those of chromium and aluminum; it consists in the double decomposition between barium oxalate and ferric sulfate in the presence of potassium oxalate.

Prepare some freshly precipitated barium oxalate by mixing solutions of barium chloride (25 grams, or 0.1 mole) and potassium oxalate (18.5 grams of the monohydrate), each one dissolved in 150 ml of hot water. Filter, wash the barium oxalate with a little hot water, and stir it into a solution of 13 grams of ferric sulfate and 20 grams of potassium oxalate in 300 ml of hot water. Leave the solution and precipitate to digest on the steam bath for two hours or more, stirring occasionally. Then filter, wash the precipitate with a little hot water, discard the precipitate, and evaporate the filterate and washings down to 50 ml, and allow to cool. Do not let the solution evaporate to dryness, and do not let it form crusts on the side of the evaporating dish at the end of the evaporation; white crusts or crystals of excess potassium oxalate contained in the solution will contaminate the product if these precautions are not taken. The product should be homogeneous, rather large green crystals. (It is easy to grow large well-formed crystals of this salt, which belongs to the monoclinic system.) Dry the crystals in the air, record the yield, and compare it with the theoretical. To find the theoretical yield, write the equations for the reactions and calculate the number of moles of each substance taken; calculate the yield on the basis of the substance present in the smallest equivalent proportion. The observed yield should be at least 80 per cent of the theoretical.

Make a small amount of approximately 0.1M solution of this salt. Place equal volumes of this solution and of 0.05M ferric sulfate solution in two test tubes side by side. Both solutions contain the same concentration of iron. Add the same amount of potassium thiocyanate solution to each. Repeat with 0.05M ferric ammonium sulfate. Note the colors before and after adding thiocyanate, and explain.

(B) *Other ferric complexes.* In three test tubes place a few milliliters of dilute (0.02-molar or less) solutions of ferric sulfate, ferric nitrate, and ferric chloride. Note their colors, and add to the three tubes 6N sulfuric, nitric, and hydrochloric acids, respectively. Divide the solution of ferric chloride in hydrochloric acid into three parts. To one portion add one-quarter its volume of sirupy phosphoric acid, and to another add a gram or so of potassium fluoride, shaking till it dissolves. Keep the third portion as a control. You now have five solutions. Note their colors; then add to each a little potassium thiocyanate. If two test tubes seem to be giving an equally dark color, dilute the solutions by equal amounts and see if you notice any difference. Record the results of the tests in tabular form, thus:

Solution	Color	Reagent added	Color produced by reagent	Color with KCNS
Fe₂(SO₄)₃	. . . . .	H₂SO₄	. . . . .	. . . . .
Fe(NO₃)₃	. . . . .	HNO₃	. . . . .	. . . . .
FeCl₃	. . . . .	HCl	. . . . .	. . . . .
FeCl₃ + HCl	. . . . .	H₃PO₄	. . . . .	. . . . .
		KF	. . . . .	. . . . .

QUESTIONS

1. In Part B, what changes were brought about by sulfuric, nitric, hydrochloric, and phosphoric acids and potassium fluoride? Write equations.

2. What is the color of the ferric ion? To what is the brown color of a solution of ferric sulfate in water due?

3. List in decreasing order of stability the complex ferric ions studied in this experiment. Do not include the thiocyanate complex.

4. (a) How does oxalic acid remove a rust stain from cloth? (b) Knowing that ordinary writing ink contains ferrous tannate which forms

black ferric tannate on exposure to air and light, how would you remove ink stains?

5. The anion of potassium cobaltic oxalate, $K_3Co(C_2O_4)_3$, has been resolved into optically active forms. Explain why this is possible.

10. Complex Salts of Tripositive Cobalt: Part 1

The simple salts of cobalt are almost exclusively those $+2$ cobalt, for example, $CoCl_2$, $CoSO_4$. Only a very few simple salts of $+3$ cobalt are known, and those, such as CoF_3 and $Co_2(SO_4)_3$, are very powerful oxidizing agents. The complex salts of tripositive cobalt, on the other hand, are extremely stable and not easily reduced. Cobalt forms an extremely large number of 6-coordinated octahedral complexes, which have been studied more extensively than the complexes of any other element. These studies have been highly significant in explaining the nature of coordination compounds and complex ions.[1] In the light of modern valence theory it is easy to see why cobalt should form 6-coordinated compounds so readily and why these should be derived from trivalent rather than divalent cobalt. The neutral cobalt atom has 27 electrons. If we remove three electrons to form a cobaltic ion and then add two electrons for each of the six coordinating groups, we have now $27 - 3 + 12 = 36$ electrons in the electron shells of the cobalt atom. This arrangement is the same as in the next inert gas, krypton, and is therefore very stable. Remembering that 6 is the natural coordination number of the cobalt atom (see Chapter V), we have a very good explanation of the stability of the 6-coordinated compounds of tripositive cobalt.

We shall leave open the question whether the links between the cobalt and the six surrounding atoms are single or double or whether they are ionic. In the majority of complexes, such as $[Co(NH_3)_6]^{+++}$, the links between cobalt and nitrogen must be single coordinate linkages. In $[Co(NO_2)_6]^=$, double bonds (with two pairs of electrons) between cobalt and nitrogen are believed to exist, whereas the complex ion $[CoF_6]^=$ is shown by its magnetic moment to be simply a triply charged cobaltic ion surrounded by

[1] The classic work in this subject is A. Werner's *Neuere Anschauungen auf dem Gebiete der anorganischen Chemie*, Braunschweig, 1919.

six fluoride ions, the electrostatic forces being very strong on account of the smallness of the fluoride ion and serving to make the complex extremely stable.

Six-coordinated complexes may be formed between the cobaltic ion and any atoms, molecules, or ions, which are sufficiently electronegative, such as NH_3, OH_2, $C_2O_4^=$, $SO_4^=$, F^-, Cl^-, Br^-, and which can donate the necessary pair of electrons. The less electronegative the group, the harder it is to introduce and the easier it is to displace; thus, though six fluorine atoms may enter into coordination, only two chlorine atoms and only two bromine atoms may enter, and iodine cannot enter at all. A weakly electronegative group like the carbonate ion is easily displaced from the coordination shell (see Experiment 11, following), whereas NH_3, a strongly electronegative group, is very hard to displace. $[Co(NH_3)_6]Cl_3$, to be prepared in this exercise, can be refluxed with constant-boiling hydrochloric acid for hours without any of the coordinated ammonia being displaced. The compound $[Co(NH_3)_5Cl]Cl_2$ can be made by heating $[Co(NH_3)_6]Cl_3$ in a sealed tube with concentrated hydrochloric acid, but it is much more easily prepared by the indirect method described in Experiment 11. Once the chlorine has entered the coordination shell, it is very hard to get out again. Silver nitrate solution precipitates the two chloride ions in $[Co(NH_3)_5Cl]Cl_2$ that are not coordinated, but it does not precipitate the third, which is bound directly to the cobalt and which may be displaced by the somewhat more electronegative NH_3, but only by heating with concentrated aqueous ammonia in a closed vessel under pressure.

The 6-coordinated compounds of tripositive cobalt are all octahedral, with the coordinated atoms at the six corners of an octahedron and the cobalt atom at the center. This arrangement has been demonstrated by X-ray diffraction and has also been proved by a study of isomerism in 6-coordinated cobaltic compounds. An ion $[CoX_5Y]$ has no isomers. $[CoX_4Y_2]$ has two isomers, *cis* and *trans*. If the complex were hexagonal and flat like a benzene ring, it would have to have three isomers.

$[CoZ_3]$, where Z is a bifunctional coordinating group like $\begin{array}{l} COO \\ | \\ COO \end{array}$ or

$\begin{array}{l} CH_2NH_2 \\ | \\ CH_2NH_2 \end{array}$, exists in optical isomers, dextro and levo, which can be resolved by the usual methods. All these facts are consistent with an octahedral model.

The general method of preparation of tripositive cobalt complexes is to oxidize a cobaltous salt in the presence of the appropriate complex-forming substances. Thus the *cobaltammines*, which contain coordinated ammonia, are made by oxidizing a solution of a cobaltous salt in excess of ammonia. Chlorides, such as ammonium chloride, are added if a complex containing chlorine is desired, and so on. The oxidizing agent is generally air or hydrogen peroxide, and it has recently been shown by Bjerrum that the oxidation is greatly speeded if activated carbon is used as a catalyst. The reaction generally yields a mixture of complex salts, but by choosing the right composition of the solution it is sometimes possible to get a good yield of the complex desired. One complex may also be obtained from another by double decomposition in many cases, as in Experiment 12.

Hexamminecobaltic chloride, $[Co(NH_3)_6]Cl_3$.[2] Mix 24 grams (0.1 mole) of cobalt chloride hexahydrate, $CoCl_2 \cdot 6H_2O$, and 16 grams (0.3 mole) of ammonium chloride with 20 ml of water and stir until most of the salts have dissolved; then add 50 ml of concentrated ammonia solution and 0.5 gram of activated carbon or decolorizing charcoal, preferably a good grade taken from a freshly opened bottle. Put the solution into a 250-ml Büchner flask which is fitted with a one-hole rubber stopper carrying a wide glass (10-mm bore) reaching down to the bottom of the flask. With the aspirator pump attached to the side arm of the flask, draw air through the solution at a brisk rate. There must be a check valve or large empty bottle between the aspirator pump and the reaction flask to prevent water sucking back from the aspirator in the event that the air inlet becomes clogged with crystals.

After an hour or an hour and a half the color of the solution in the flask should have changed from a reddish color to a yellowish brown. The color may easily be observed by swirling the liquid round the sides of the flask while holding against the light. Pass air for 10 minutes after all the red color has gone from the liquid; then filter the solution on a Büchner funnel. The product, mixed with carbon, remains on the filter paper.

[2] N. Bjerrum and J. P. McReynolds, *Inorganic Syntheses*, Vol. 2, page 217.

Stir the filter cake into 150 ml of water to which has been added 2 ml of concentrated hydrochloric acid. This should be enough to give the solution a slight acid reaction after all the solid has been added. Test the solution with litmus; if necessary, add a few more drops of hydrochloric acid. Then heat to 50–60° and filter while hot. The desired product is in the solution. It may be precipitated by using the common-ion effect. Add 30 ml of concentrated hydrochloric acid to the hot solution and set aside to cool slowly. When it has cooled to room temperature, set the beaker in crushed ice and cool to 0°. Filter the fine yellow crystals on a Büchner funnel; then wash, first with 50 ml of 60 per cent alcohol and then with 50 ml of 95 per cent alcohol. Suck as dry as possible; then dry on a watch glass in the oven at 80°. The yield should be about 85 per cent.

The carbon catalyst used in this preparation not only catalyzes the oxidation but also catalyzes the attainment of the equilibrium

$$[Co(NH_3)_5Cl]^{++} + NH_3 \rightleftharpoons [Co(NH_3)_6]^{+++} + Cl^-$$

which under the conditions of the reaction is greatly in favor of the desired $[Co(NH_3)_6]^{+++}$.

Determination of purity. The purity of the product may be tested by determining the percentage of ionized chloride. This testing may be done gravimetrically by precipitation with silver nitrate, but volumetric methods are faster and are adequate here. Titration with silver nitrate is not easy, since none of the usual indicators work satisfactorily in the solution of the hexamminecobaltic salt; however, the chloride can be easily and accurately titrated with mercuric nitrate.

Mercuric nitrate is well ionized in solution, but mercuric chloride is not. When, therefore, mercuric nitrate is run into a solution containing chloride ions, the mercuric ion concentration in the solution remains extremely low so long as there is any chloride left. Sodium nitroprusside is added as an indicator to tell when excess of mercuric ions is present. Mercuric nitroprusside is insoluble and separates as a white turbidity at the end point.[3]

Prepare the following solutions: (a) Mercuric nitrate, 0.1N.

[3] See I. M. Kolthoff, and E. B. Sandell, *Textbook of Quantitative Inorganic Analysis*, Chapter XXXV. New York: Macmillan, 1943.

$Hg(NO_3)_2]\frac{1}{2}H_2O$, 8.5 grams, plus 5 ml 6M nitric acid, is dissolved in water and made up to 500 ml. *This solution must be standardized.* (b) Potassium chloride, 0.1N. Dry this salt at 110° for several hours and cool in a desiccator, and weigh out accurately the appropriate amount to prepare 250 or 500 ml of solution; dissolve in water, transfer to the volumetric flask, make up to the mark. (c) Sodium nitroprusside, 10 per cent. This solution should be fresh; that is, it should not be kept for more than a week. (d) Hexamminecobaltic chloride. Weigh out accurately about 0.9 gram of salt, dissolve in water, and make up to 100 ml in a volumetric flask.

To standardize the mercuric nitrate, pipette 10 ml of 0.1N potassium chloride into a 250-ml Erlenmeyer flask; then add 40 ml of water (measured with a graduate) and 3 drops of 10 per cent sodium nitroprusside. Titrate with mercuric nitrate, shaking well between additions as the end point is neared. The end point is marked by a permanent white turbidity and is quite sharp. When the mercuric nitrate has been standardized, titrate the hexamminecobaltic chloride solution by the same procedure, taking care to have the volume of solution in the titration flask the same as in the standardization. The end point arrives somewhat early because of the reaction $HgCl_2 + Hg^{++} \rightarrow 2HgCl^+$; but by performing the standardization and titration under similar conditions, with the final mercuric chloride concentrations almost the same, this error, which is small in any case, becomes quite negligible.

The product should be at least 98 or 99 per cent pure according to this titration.

Tests

1. To a 1 per cent solution of the salt add a little saturated ammonium oxalate solution. Note that hexamminecobaltic oxalate is almost insoluble in cold water.

2. Heat a little of the salt with concentrated hydrochloric acid for a few minutes. Note whether any change occurs which might indicate removal of ammonia from the compound.

3. Heat a little of the salt with concentrated sodium hydroxide solution, and note whether any ammonia is given off.

4. Heat a little of the salt in a dry test tube over a Bunsen burner until there is no further change. Identify the products as far as possible.

The solubility of hexamminecobaltic chloride in water is 7.0 grams per 100 ml of solution at 20°. Calculate the solubility product and, neglecting activity coefficients, calculate the solubility in 2.0-molar hydrochloric acid.

11. Complex Salts of Tripositive Cobalt: Part 2

In this experiment carbonate ion is first introduced into the coordination shell and is displaced afterward by ammonia and chloride ion together.

(A) *Carbonatotetrammine cobaltic nitrate*, $[Co(NH_3)_4CO_3]NO_3 \cdot \frac{1}{2}H_2O$. Dissolve 50 grams of ammonium carbonate in 250 ml of water and add 125 ml of concentrated ammonia. Then add, with stirring, 25 grams of cobaltous nitrate, $Co(NO_3)_2 \cdot 6H_2O$, dissolved in 50 ml of water. Draw a stream of air through the solution for 3 hours. During this time the color changes from blue (cobaltous) to deep red (cobaltic). When no further change is apparent, pour the solution into an evaporating dish or dishes and concentrate to 150 ml, adding 10 to 12 grams of ammonium carbonate in small portions during the evaporation. Filter if necessary, then evaporate to 100 ml, adding 3 grams of ammonium carbonate a little at a time. Cool; purplish-red crystals will separate. Cool them in ice before filtering them off. Obtain some more crystals by evaporating the mother liquor almost to dryness, cooling to room temperature and extracting with 15 times its weight of water. Filter the solution, and precipitate the salt by adding twice the volume of alcohol. The yield of combined products is approximately 8 grams, or half the theoretical.

(B) *Chloropentammine cobaltic chloride*, $[Co(NH_3)_5Cl]Cl_2$. Dissolve 6 grams of the product just obtained, $[Co(NH_3)_4CO_3]NO_3 \cdot 0.5H_2O$, in 80 ml of water and add concentrated hydrochloric acid until all the carbon dioxide is expelled—about 10 ml will be required. Neutralize with concentrated ammonia and add 10 ml excess ammonia. Heat on the steam bath for 45 minutes. During this stage, aquapentammine cobaltic chloride, $[Co(NH_3)_5H_2O]Cl_3$, is produced. Cool, and add 100 ml of concentrated hydrochloric acid; heat again on the steam bath for an hour, thus displacing the coordinated water by chlorine. Cool the solution in ice, filter off the salt and wash with a few milliliters of ice water, then with alcohol. Dry at 80 to 100°. The yield is about 4 grams of purple-red crystals, often called purpureocobaltic chloride.

Tests

1. Determine the percentage of ionized chloride in the second product by weighing out accurately about 1.3 grams, dissolving in water and making up to 100 ml in a volumetric flask, and then titrating 10-ml portions with mercuric nitrate as described in Experiment 10.

2. Treat small portions of carbonatotetrammine cobaltic nitrate with dilute hydrochloric, sulfuric, and acetic acids. Account for the difference in behavior.

3. Dissolve a little chloropentammine cobaltic chloride in warm water and immediately add silver nitrate in excess. Do not boil. When the silver chloride begins to coagulate and settle, filter. Take a portion of the clear filtrate, add dilute nitric acid, and boil. Explain the appearance of a precipitate.

QUESTIONS

1. The percentage of chloride ion found in the chloropentammine salt was probably higher than the theoretical. What is the most likely impurity?

2. How could you distinguish the two salts prepared in this exercise by conductivity measurements?

3. Why does not nickel form compounds corresponding to the cobaltammines?

12. Complex Salts of Tripositive Cobalt: Part 3[4]

This exercise illustrates a rather unusual type of isomerism. Isomeric nitrites and nitro compounds are well known in organic chemistry but are rarely met in inorganic chemistry. However, isomeric nitro- and nitrito-cobaltammines are known and will be prepared here. The starting point is chloropentammine cobaltic chloride, $[Co(NH_3)_5Cl]Cl_2$, prepared in the last experiment.

(A) $[Co(NH_3)_5NO_2]Cl_2$. Dissolve 1.5 grams of chloropentammine cobaltic chloride in 15 ml of water to which 5 ml of 6M ammonia has been added. Warm on the water bath until the

4 S. M. Jorgensen, *Z. Anorg. Chem.*, **5** (1894), 168, and **17** (1898), 463.

salt dissolves, then filter, cool, and acidify *slightly* with dilute hydrochloric acid. Add 2 grams of sodium nitrite; heat the solution slightly until the red precipitate first formed has dissolved. Cool and add 20 ml of concentrated hydrochloric acid— carefully, since considerable effervescence occurs. Cool the solution in ice, filter off the yellow-brown crystals, and wash with alcohol.

(B) $[CO(NH_3)_5ONO]Cl_2$. Dissolve 1.5 grams of chloropentammine cobaltic chloride in 25 ml of water to which 5 ml of concentrated ammonia has been added, warming gently if necessary. Filter, and add 6M hydrochloric acid carefully until the solution is just neutral to litmus. Add 1.5 grams of sodium nitrite to the cold solution, then 1.5 ml of 6M hydrochloric acid, and leave to stand in the cold for an hour or so. A salmon-pink precipitate slowly forms. This, the desired product, is a good deal less soluble than the isomeric nitro compound. Cool in ice, filter, and wash with ice water and alcohol.

When the salt is dry, put a little in a dry test tube and warm it by waving it above a Bunsen burner flame. The salt changes from salmon pink to brownish yellow, which after cooling is identical with the color of the product in (A). The nitrite isomer has been converted to the more stable nitro form. This change takes place in a few days of standing at room temperature.

QUESTIONS

1. Suggest names for the two compounds you have prepared.

2. Can you think of any other case of structural isomerism in simple inorganic nitrogen compounds?

3. It is claimed that nine different compounds exist having the empirical formula $Co(NH_3)_3(NO_2)_3$. Write structural formulas for six, recognizing that the molecular formula may be twice the empirical formula in some of them.

13. Nickel Carbonyl[5]

A number of the transition metals combine with carbon monoxide to form compounds known as the carbonyls. These are all more or less unstable, and most of them require high pres-

[5] *Inorganic Syntheses*, **2**, 234.
Reviews of metal carbonyls: A. A. Blanchard, *Chem. Rev.*, **21** (1937), 3, and **26** (1940); W. Wardlaw, *Ann. Reports of Chem. Soc.*, **31** (1934), 99.

sures of carbon monoxide for their formation. Only elements with even atomic numbers form simple carbonyls having only one atom of metal in the molecule; in the first long period, the simple carbonyls known are $Cr(CO)_6$, $Fe(CO)_5$, and $Ni(CO)_4$. Carbonyls are to be considered as coordination compounds in which the carbon monoxide molecule, probably through the carbon, donates a pair of electrons to the metal atom. It will be noticed that if we add two electrons from each CO molecule to the electrons in the metal atoms, we have 36 electrons in each case; this is the number of electrons in the atom of the next inert gas, krypton. *The metal atoms in these carbonyls have an electronic configuration like that of an inert gas.* The bonding between the metal and the carbon is considered to resonate between single and double bonds.

According to this interpretation, odd-numbered elements such as cobalt cannot form simple carbonyls $M(CO)_x$, but they do form complex carbonyls, such as $Co_2(CO)_8$. These are solids, in contrast to the simple carbonyls, which are volatile liquids.

In all these compounds, some or all of the CO can be replaced by nitric oxide, NO, which is believed to donate *three* electrons to the metal. On this basis, the formation of the volatile cobalt nitrosyl carbonyl, $Co(CO)_3NO$, is easily understood.

Nickel carbonyl is prepared in this experiment, since it is the easiest of the carbonyls to prepare, no high pressure being needed, and is of industrial importance in the Mond process for the purification of nickel.

The apparatus is shown in Fig. 12. The connections between vessels A, B, and C must be all glass. No rubber may be used. Sealed connections are best, but ground-glass joints lubricated with a mixture of 1 part paraffin to 3 parts vaseline may also be used. *Avoid leakage of nickel carbonyl into the room;* it is extremely poisonous, inflicting permanent damage to the body through deposition of colloidal nickel in the organs, and the smell is not strong enough to give due warning of its presence. The apparatus should therefore be set up in the hood. The gases pass out of the reaction system through a mercury bubbler or check valve to a glass capillary outlet inserted into the air intake of a lighted Bunsen burner. The flame will burn up any nickel carbonyl and will also be colored a brilliant gray by it.

Vessel A is about 25 mm in diameter, has a glass-wool plug in the bottom, and is filled to a depth of about 7 cm with nickel formate crystals that have been mixed with about 1 per cent by weight of mercuric oxide.   It is immmersed in an oil bath.   The tube C is loosely packed with pieces of broken glass or porcelain for part of its length.   The two stopcocks at the intake of A are connected to sources of hydrogen and carbon monoxide.   Tank hydrogen should be freed from traces of oxygen by passing it over red-hot copper and then through a phosphorus pentoxide tube.

First displace the air from all parts of the apparatus, including the carbon monoxide intake, and pass hydrogen slowly.   Heat

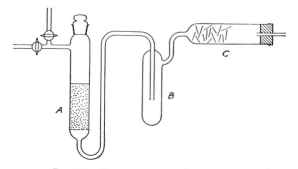

Fig. 12.   Preparation of nickel carbonyl.

the oil bath, raising the temperature slowly from 100° to about 190 or 200°, until the green nickel formate begins to go black because of decomposition to metallic nickel.   The water of crystallization of the nickel formate is meanwhile carried away by the hydrogen stream; to avoid condensation of this water in B and C, this trap and tube should be kept heated during the decomposition.   Nickel formate decomposes on heating, mainly into $Ni + CO_2 + H_2$; however, a certain amount of water and CO are formed as well.   *Do not heat the nickel formate or nickel above 200°, or the reactivity of the nickel will be reduced.*

When the reduction to metallic nickel is complete, remove the oil bath and let the tube A cool to room temperature, passing hydrogen continuously.   Place a Dewar vessel with dry ice and acetone around the trap B.   When A has cooled, turn off the hydrogen and pass carbon monoxide rapidly.   Watch the mercury bubbler carefully; if the mercury sucks back too far, turn on the carbon monoxide faster and nearly close the pinch clamp on the rubber tube leading from the bubbler. *Do not let air suck back into the reaction system.*

Nickel carbonyl condenses in the trap B as a white solid. When the reaction is over, reduce the carbon monoxide flow to a very slow rate and let the contents of B thaw out. Mark the level of the liquid in the trap with a gummed label, and afterward measure the volume and calculate the yield. The specific gravity of nickel carbonyl is 1.31 at room temperature.

Now warm the tube C gently with a flame until it is just too hot to touch—between 50 and 100°—and increase the flow of carbon monoxide. Nickel carbonyl vapor is carried over and decomposes in C, depositing a mirror of nickel on the surfaces. The principle of the Mond process for purifying nickel is to pass carbon monoxide over the metal and then to decompose the nickel carbonyl on the surface of heated nickel balls. Cobalt, the main impurity to be removed, does not react with carbon monoxide under these conditions, and in any case its carbonyl is not volatile. Nickel completely free from cobalt is thus obtained.

Before the liquid carbonyl in B is all gone, pass some nitric oxide into it. The nitric oxide may be prepared as in Experiment 24 and stored over water, but it must be dried by sulfuric acid before being used for this purpose. Pass it in through the stopcock originally used for hydrogen and let it flow slowly for about half an hour. A complex solid nickel nitrosyl carbonyl should form in the liquid in B.

If pure liquid nickel carbonyl is wanted for any purpose, the tube C is dispensed with and arrangements are made to transfer the carbonyl from the trap to an appropriate receiver. Nickel carbonyl oxidizes spontaneously in air, but if a little oxidation is not harmful it may be poured quickly from one vessel to another in the air, *but only in a good draft.* Nickel carbonyl is very volatile at room temperature, and, as has been said, the vapor is extremely poisonous.

QUESTION

This experiment describes a way of getting nickel that is free from cobalt. Another experiment in this manual indicates a way in which cobalt compounds free from nickel can be obtained. What is this experiment? Show, from the electronic structures of cobalt and nickel, that nickel can form no such compounds as the cobalt compounds referred to.

14. Hydrobromic Acid[6]

Of the various methods for making hydrogen bromide, the direct catalyzed union of hydrogen and bromine is one of the most convenient. The reaction

$$H_2 + Br_2 \rightarrow 2HBr$$

has not the violence of the hydrogen-chlorine reaction, yet it proceeds virtually to completion under easily obtainable conditions. A platinum catalyst and a temperature of 250° are used.

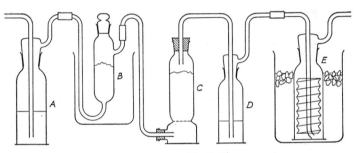

Fig. 13. Preparation of hydrobromic acid.

In this experiment an aqueous solution of hydrobromic acid will be prepared.

Set up the apparatus shown in Fig. 13. Hydrogen is obtained from a cylinder. The bromine bubbler A should have a volume of about 200 ml; B, the catalyst chamber, is made of Pyrex glass, about 25 mm in diameter and long enough to hold a catalyst mass some 10 cm long. The absorption tower C, about 20 cm high, contains red phosphorus supported on glass wool or glass beads; its function is to react with any bromine which escapes conversion to HBr in the catalyst chamber. D is a small bubbler containing some 10 to 20 ml of water, to absorb phosphorus tribromide vapor from C. The washing bottle E, which should preferably be of the type with a glass spiral inside to give the gas longer contact with the water, contains distilled water to absorb the hydrogen bromide. The catalyst chamber is surrounded by an

[6] *Inorganic Syntheses*, **1**, 152; *Organic Syntheses*, **15**, 35. The author is also indebted to Professor H. B. Van Valkenburgh for details of this preparation.

oil bath that can be heated; the absorption bottle E is placed in a vessel that can be filled with crushed ice.

The catalyst in B is platinized asbestos. It is most economical to purchase this commercially, but it can be made in the laboratory by boiling short-fiber asbestos in concentrated hydrochloric acid, then sucking it as dry as possible on a Büchner funnel, dipping it in a 5 per cent solution of chlorplatinic acid, draining off surplus solution, then heating on a sand bath in a covered dish with a little ammonium chloride until no more ammonium chloride fumes appear. Platinized silica gel can also be used; it offers less resistance to gas flow than asbestos, but for the quantities to be prepared in this experiment this advantage is immaterial. Palladized asbestos may also be used, though it is a little too active to control easily. The bromine bubbler A should preferably have a ground-glass head, since bromine slowly attacks rubber. The connection between A and B if of rubber tubing, should be made as short as possible; neoprene tubing is better.

The bromine should be at a temperature between 25 and 30° during the experiment to give the necessary vapor pressure. If the room temperature is less than 25°, surround the bromine bubbler with a bath of warm water.

At the start of the experiment put 50 ml of bromine in A, and weigh the bubbler and contents. Put about 150 ml of distilled water in E and surround E by crushed ice. Secure the tops of the bubblers, catalyst chamber, and absorption tower with strong rubber bands or wire, so that they will not be blown out by the pressure of the hydrogen stream.

Do not heat the oil bath surrounding the catalyst chamber until you have displaced the air from it by hydrogen; otherwise there is danger of explosion. Lead the excess hydrogen, passing out through E, into the draft or out of doors so that it cannot accumulate and cause an explosion.

First pass the hydrogen for a minute or two to displace the air, then reduce the flow so that the gas is passing very slowly, and heat the oil bath to 230–250°. Now increase the hydrogen flow until it is bubbling so fast that you can hardly count the drops. Adjust it so that the gas coming out of the catalyst chamber does not have more than a faint yellowish-brown tinge due to unreacted bromine.

Continue the hydrogen flow for about two hours, or until most of the bromine has gone from A. Reduce the hydrogen flow to about two bubbles a second or less, and take away the oil bath from under the catalyst chamber; after a minute or two replace it by a beaker of cold water. When the catalyst is quite cool, stop the hydrogen flow and disconnect A and E. Weigh A again; the loss in weight of A is the quantity of bromine used. Pour the solution of hydrobromic acid from E into a graduated cylinder and note the volume. Titrate 1-ml portions with 0.2M sodium hydroxide solution. Calculate the amount of hydrobromic acid in the solution and compute the percentage yield.

If desired, constant-boiling hydrobromic acid may be obtained by distillation of this solution. At 760 mm the constant-boiling mixture contains 47.8 per cent of HBr and boils at 126°C.

QUESTIONS

1. Why cannot hydrogen bromide be made like hydrogen chloride, by heating sodium bromide with concentrated sulfuric acid?

2. Under what conditions could you expect to get pure aqueous hydrobromic acid from sodium bromide and sulfuric acid?

3. Give the equations for three other methods of preparing hydrogen bromide.

15. Boron Trifluoride[7]

Boron trifluoride, BF_3, is a gas remarkable for the many addition compounds it forms with compounds of oxygen, nitrogen, sulfur, and other elements—even with the inert gases. The electronic structure,

$$: \overset{..}{\underset{}{F}} :$$
$$\overset{..}{\underset{..}{B}} : \overset{..}{\underset{..}{F}} :$$
$$: \overset{..}{\underset{..}{F}} :$$

shows that the electron shell of boron is incomplete, with room for another pair of electrons. That is, it is an acceptor molecule, and its addition compounds are all formed by donation of a pair of electrons from the other molecule to form a coordinate link with

[7] *Inorganic Syntheses*, **1**, 21, and **2**, 23.
F. J. Sowa and J. A. Nieuwland, *J. Am. Chem. Soc.*, **58** (1936), 272.

the boron. They are among the simplest types of coordination compound (see Chapter 5). The compound with ammonia, for example, which will be prepared in this exercise, has the structure

$$
\begin{array}{l}
\ \ \ \ \ \ \ \ \ \ \overset{\cdot\cdot}{} \\
\text{H} : \ddot{\text{F}} : \\
\overset{\cdot\cdot}{} \ \ \overset{\cdot\cdot}{} \ \ \overset{\cdot\cdot}{} \\
\text{H} : \ddot{\text{N}} : \ddot{\text{B}} : \ddot{\text{F}} : \quad \text{or} \quad \text{H}_3\text{N} \rightarrow \text{BF}_3 \\
\overset{\cdot\cdot}{} \ \ \overset{\cdot\cdot}{} \ \ \overset{\cdot\cdot}{} \\
\text{H} : \ddot{\text{F}} : \\
\overset{\cdot\cdot}{}
\end{array}
$$

Because of its electron-accepting power, boron trifluoride is an excellent catalyst for many reactions such as alkylations and polymerizations. It is prepared in considerable quantities for use in the petroleum and synthetic organic chemical industries.

Boron trifluoride is similar in many ways to silicon tetra-fluoride, including its physical properties and reactions with water and alkalies. It could be prepared by an analogous method:

$$\text{SiO}_2 + 2\text{H}_2\text{SO}_4 + 2\text{CaF}_2 \rightarrow 2\text{CaSO}_4 + \text{SiF}_4 + \text{H}_2\text{O}$$
$$\text{B}_2\text{O}_3 + 3\text{H}_2\text{SO}_4 + 3\text{CaF}_2 \rightarrow 3\text{CaSO}_4 + 2\text{BF}_3 + 3\text{H}_2\text{O}$$

However, a smoother reaction which gives a purer product, less contaminated by silicon tetrafluoride, is the following:

$$\text{B}_2\text{O}_3 + 6\text{NH}_4\text{BF}_4 + 3\text{H}_2\text{SO}_4 \rightarrow 8\text{BF}_3 + 3(\text{NH}_4)_2\text{SO}_4 + 3\text{H}_2\text{O}$$

and this reaction will be used here. First, boric oxide and ammonium fluoborate must be prepared, since these are not generally available. (Any soluble fluoborate could be used in place of the ammonium salt.)

Boric oxide. Heat 30 grams of boric acid in an iron dish over a Meker burner, stirring occasionally with an old file, until a clear viscous melt is obtained. Cool quickly, break out the glassy mass, crush it in a rock crusher or other device (it is very hard and brittle, so do not attempt this preliminary crushing in an ordinary mortar); then grind to a powder in a large iron mortar.

Ammonium fluoborate. Grind up 65 grams (1.15 moles) of ammonium acid fluoride, NH_4HF_2, with 30 grams (0.5 mole) of boric acid, and heat the mixture in a shallow iron dish over a gas ring or large burner flame in the hood. Frothing occurs, ammonia and steam escape, and the excess of NH_4HF_2 is volatilized. Continue to heat until a dry, puffed-up white mass remains.

Break this up with a pestle and heat again, but stop as soon as dense white fumes indicate that the main product is starting to sublime. Cool; then powder in a mortar.

This product is pure enough for use in preparing boron trifluoride. If a clean, pure preparation of ammonium fluoborate is required for another purpose, the best way to make it is to mix the theoretical amounts of ammonium acid fluoride and boric acid in aqueous solution in a plastic dish, and evaporate to crystallization on a steam bath.[8]

Boron trifluoride. Set up in the hood the apparatus shown in Fig. 14. Since boron trifluoride attacks cork less than it does

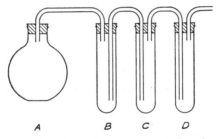

A   B   C   D

Fig. 14. Preparation of boron trifluoride.

rubber, cork stoppers should be used and rubber connections avoided as far as possible. (Where a very pure product is desired, an all-glass apparatus must be used. Ground joints may be lubricated with a paraffin-vaseline mixture.) The vessels and connections should be of Pyrex glass.

The generating flask A has a volume of 500 ml. The test tubes B, C, and D are 25 × 200 mm. B is empty and used as a trap; C contains some 30 ml of sulfuric acid saturated with boric acid, to absorb hydrogen fluoride from the gas stream. In A, place the entire product of ammonium fluoborate, well mixed with 6 grams of finely powdered boric oxide. In D, place 30 ml of diethyl ether, and cool the tube in ice. Arrange for the gas passing out of D to be sucked away by the draft or to be absorbed in caustic soda as in Experiment 1.

When all is ready, pour 40 ml of concentrated sulfuric acid into flask A and replace the cork immediately. A vigorous reaction occurs, which, however, soon slackens and must be maintained

[8] *Inorganic Syntheses*, **2**, 23.

by heating. Keep the reaction going steadily but not too fast. Some of the boron trifluoride is absorbed by the ether in *D*, forming a viscous solution of the addition compound $(C_2H_5)_2O\cdot BF_3$. This will be used for the tests to follow.

Before all the boron trifluoride has been generated, replace the test tube of ether with a test tube containing a few milliliters of water. Note the reaction between boron trifluoride and water. If sufficient gas is passed, viscous liquids $BF_3\cdot2H_2O$ and $BF_3\cdot H_2O$ are obtained. These liquids are strongly acidic, the latter ionizing to H^+ and $HO\cdot BF_3^-$. Similar compounds are formed from boron trifluoride and alcohols.

Pass a little boron trifluoride gas into a Bunsen flame. Note the characteristic color, which is given by all volatile boron compounds and is a sensitive test for boron.

Tests

Perform the following tests on the boron trifluoride-ether solution:

1. Pass ammonia gas into 10 ml of the solution. The ammonia can be drawn from a cylinder or prepared by dropping concentrated aqueous ammonia onto sodium hydroxide pellets and drying the gas by contact with potassium hydroxide sticks or pellets. The white precipitate is the complex $NH_3\cdot BF_3$. Filter the solid on a Büchner funnel, wash it with a little ether, and allow it to dry. Heat the solid in a dry test tube; it sublimes unchanged.

2. Mix a few drops of the solution with a few drops of pyridine. Note that a similar addition product is formed.

3. In a small distilling flask mix 10 ml of the solution with 12 ml of acetic anhydride. Reflux the mixture for 10 minutes, then distill slowly, collecting the distillate which comes over between 65 and 100°. It should be mainly ethyl acetate, formed by the reaction

$$(CH_3COO)_2 + (C_2H_5)_2O \rightarrow 2CH_3COOC_2H_5$$

Wash the distillate with about 50 ml of 10 per cent sodium carbonate to free it from boron trifluoride and any acetic anhyride; collect the ethyl acetate with a separatory funnel, noting its smell and its volume. The yield would be practically theoretical, except that some of the ethyl acetate remains behind in the distilling flask as the very stable complex $CH_3COOC_2H_5 \cdot BF_3$.

Make the following test with the aqueous solution of boron trifluoride: Test for fluoride ion by diluting with water, neutralizing with sodium bicarbonate, making slightly acid with acetic acid, and adding calcium chloride solution.

A striking test of the catalytic power of boron trifluoride can be made if the materials are available. Condense some isobutylene in a beaker surrounded by dry ice, or simply put some pieces of dry ice in a beaker and pass in gaseous isobutylene; then add a few drops of isoprene. Stir the liquid mush and pass in boron trifluoride. Immediately a solid white mass of butyl rubber is formed.[9]

QUESTIONS

1. Compare the reactions of BF_3 and SiF_4 on water.

2. Compare the properties of BF_3 and BCl_3. To what do you attribute the differences?

3. A small amount of hydrofluoric acid is added to a solution containing a borate and a silicate, and the solution is evaporated with sulfuric acid. Which will be driven off, BF_3 or SiF_4?[10]

16. Aluminum Bromide

This preparation must be performed in the hood.

Fit a dry 150-ml distilling flask with a cork (not rubber) stopper carrying a small separatory funnel. In the flask put 6 grams of aluminum turnings, packed down fairly tightly, and in the funnel place 40 grams (13 ml) of bromine. Also get ready a dry test tube, fitted with a cork, to receive the aluminum bromide. Weigh this tube and cork before you start.

With the distilling flask clamped vertically, run in the bromine, *drop by drop*, over a period of about an hour. As the bromine strikes the aluminum it reacts very vigorously. If the reaction becomes too energetic, stop adding the bromine. When all the

[9] For a review of the addition complexes and catalytic properties of boron trifluoride, see *Annual Reports of the Chemical Society*, 1942, page 128; also the papers of Nieuwland and coworkers in *J. Am. Chem. Soc.*, 1931 and following years.

[10] This procedure gives a quantitative separation suitable for analytical purposes. See W. T. Schrenk and W. H. Ode, *Ind. Eng. Chem. (Anal.)*, 1 (1929), 201.

bromine has been added, remove the cork and separatory funnel, insert a thermometer reading to 300°C in the cork, replace
the cork, and distill the aluminum bromide, heating the flask with
a bare flame. No condenser is needed; the side arm of the distilling flask acts as an air condenser. Use an unweighed test tube or
beaker as the receiver at first, and reject the distillate that comes
below 200°. Collect the distillate above 200° in the weighed test
tube. Continue distilling until no more aluminum bromide
comes over, and record the boiling point of aluminum bromide.
The bromide condenses as a liquid that solidifies on cooling.
Weigh the receiver and contents, and record your yield.

Tests

Make the following tests on your product:

1. Determine the melting point. Melt the product in the test
tube by placing the corked tube in boiling water, and insert a
thermometer, which must be held in place by a suitably bored
cork. Clamp the tube vertically and shield it from drafts. It is
best to support this test tube inside a larger test tube so that
there is an air space between the two tubes. Allow the material
to cool, and take temperature readings at half-minute intervals
until the material has all solidified. Plot the results on a
graph, and from the temperature-time curve find the melting
point of aluminum bromide. From the shape of your curve and
the melting point estimate the purity of your product. The
melting point of pure aluminum bromide is 97.5°; your melting
point is probably nearer 90°.

2. Study the hydrolysis of aluminum bromide as follows: First,
drop a small fragment of the solid into about 25 ml of cold
water. Note the reaction, and test the solution with litmus
and Congo red. (Congo red changes color about pH 4.) Second, pour a little melted aluminum bromide into a small dry
beaker, and rotate the beaker so that the bromide solidifies
in a film over the bottom of the beaker and some of the sides.
While it is solidifying, try to note the crystalline form. Then,
allow it to stand in a moist atmosphere for about half an hour.
There should be substantial fumes of hydrobromic acid during
these operations, though it is interesting to note that only one-third
of the bromine is liberated as HBr. Finally, add a little water to

dissolve the material. Note whether or not a clear solution is formed. What is the difference between hydrolysis by moist air and hydrolysis by an excess of water added all at once?

3. Test the solubility of aluminum bromide in carbon disulfide and benzene.

The disposal of unwanted aluminum bromide and the washing out of the reaction flask present a problem, since the reaction of this material with water is extremely violent. The vessels can be rinsed out with alcohol or, better, with a nearly saturated solution of calcium chloride.

This procedure does not give pure aluminum bromide. The product always contains unreacted bromine; moreover, there is a little reaction with the cork. It can be purified by redistilling in an all-glass apparatus in a stream of hydrogen[11] or by simply refluxing with aluminum turnings and then distilling.

QUESTIONS

1. Are metallic halides usually soluble in carbon disulfide?

2. Is anhydrous aluminum bromide predominantly ionic or covalent? Can electricity be conducted by (a) molten aluminum bromide? (b) by a solution of aluminum bromide in water?

3. Distinguish between *hydrolysis* and *hydration*, with examples.

4. Just above the boiling point of this compound, the vapor has the formula Al_2Br_6. Suggest a structural formula.[12]

17. Carbon Tetrachloride and the Chlorides of Sulfur

The commercial method of making carbon tetrachloride is to pass chlorine and carbon disulfide vapor together through a hot tube. The reaction

$$CS_2 + 3Cl_2 \rightarrow CCl_4 + S_2Cl_2$$

takes place, and the two products are separated by fractional distillation. The reaction can be made to go below 100° in the presence of a suitable catalyst or chlorine carrier.[13]

Take 100 grams (79 ml) of carbon disulfide and 0.5 gram of powdered antimony and place in a 500-ml flask with a ground-

[11] H. H. Kaveler and C. J. Monroe, *J. Am. Chem. Soc.*, **50** (1928), 2421.

[12] See K. J. Palmer and N. Elliott, *J. Am. Chem. Soc.*, **60** (1938), 1852.

[13] A. W. Hofmann, *Liebig's Annalen*, **115** (1860), 264.

glass socket. Set this flask on a steam bath in the hood and insert
a reflux condenser. Ground-glass connections must be used,
since the products attack rubber and cork. Down the inside of
the condenser place a narrow tube, drawn out to about 2 mm
diameter at the bottom and reaching nearly to the bottom of the
flask, to lead in chlorine.

Heat the flask on the steam bath until the carbon disulfide
begins to boil, then pass in dry chlorine from a cylinder. After
about 10 minutes the antimony has all reacted to form antimony
chloride, which is the catalyst for the reaction. Pass the chlorine
in briskly after this. It reacts as fast as it enters, and no chlorine
will be seen in the upper part of the condenser. Do not let the
liquid reflux too fast, or some of it will be lost.

After an hour and a half the greenish-yellow color of chlorine
gas will be seen at the top of the condenser, indicating that an
excess has been passed. The liquid in the flask will have more
than doubled in volume and should be clear yellow with perhaps
a little suspended solid. Turn off the steam and the chlorine.
If it is necessary to interrupt the experiment at this point,
cool the flask, remove the condenser, and stopper the flask
temporarily with a cork. The ground-glass joint is very apt to
"freeze" when standing in contact with sulfur chloride vapors.

Next, distill fractionally the contents of the flask. For a
fractionating column a tube 25 cm long and 22 mm in diameter
packed with $\frac{3}{8}$-in. Raschig rings does very well. Insert a thermometer at the head of the column. Collect the fractions which
boil at 55 to 70°, 70 to 80°, and 130 to 140°. The first is mainly
sulfur dichloride, SCl_2 (b.p. 59°), a deep-red fuming liquid that
dissociates on heating; the second is carbon tetrachloride (b.p.
78°) contaminated with a little sulfur chlorides and antimony
chlorides; the third is sulfur monochloride, S_2Cl_2 (b.p. 136°)
contaminated with antimony chlorides. The yellow residue in
the flask contains most of the antimony catalyst and also the
compound CCl_3SCl. The yields depend on the time for which
the chlorine was passed and the efficiency of the reflux condenser.
The carbon tetrachloride can be purified by shaking with warm
50 per cent sodium hydroxide for a few minutes, separating,
washing with water, and redistilling; the sulfur monochloride can
be freed from the antimony which it contains by cooling in ice

and shaking for a few minutes with ice-cold concentrated hydro-chloric acid.

As soon as the distillation is finished, the ground-glass joints should be taken apart to avoid their freezing. The products can be kept in cork-stoppered bottles, although the best way to store the sulfur dichloride is in a sealed bulb.

Tests

Mix small amounts of the two chlorides of sulfur with water and observe the reactions. Write equations for these reactions.

QUESTIONS

1. What catalyst could be substituted for antimony?
2. What is a preparative use for SbF_3?
3. If you only wanted S_2Cl_2, how would you prepare it?
4. What is an industrial use for S_2Cl_2?
5. Which is the more volatile, $SbCl_3$ or $SbCl_5$? Suggest a probable reason.

18. Titanium Tetrachloride

This compound is an example of a volatile, covalent metal chloride. It is prepared here by a method that can be used quite generally for making the chlorides of most metals and a few non-metals, namely, the simultaneous action of carbon and chlorine upon the oxide at a red heat. Carbon tetrachloride may be an intermediate. In fact, one variation of the method is to pass the vapor of carbon tetrachloride or of phosgene over the heated oxide. Still another method for making chlorides, similar in principle, is to pass chlorine over the heated carbide.

Set up the apparatus shown in Fig. 15. Since chlorine and titanium tetrachloride attack rubber slightly, there should be no more contact with rubber than is necessary. The chlorine must be absolutely dry; tank chlorine is satisfactory. A sulfuric acid bubbler is inserted to give an idea of the rate of flow of the chlorine. Suitable precautions must be taken to prevent the unreacted chlorine from escaping into the laboratory. The product is collected in a receiver that is cooled in ice and salt.

Mix thoroughly on a large piece of paper, or ball-mill together,

24 grams (0.30 mole) of pure powdered titanium dioxide with 8 grams of carbon black. Then, with the help of a spatula, knead the mixed powder in an iron dish with just enough cottonseed oil (about 10 grams) to make a stiff paste. Shape the paste into squares $\frac{1}{2}$ in. across, cover the iron dish with a flat piece of sheet iron, and heat in the hood over a large flame. Much of the oil is decomposed, and the gases from it burn with a large smoky flame. When no more smoke is seen and the dish is red-hot, cool to room temperature (keeping the dish covered until it is cold), and cut up

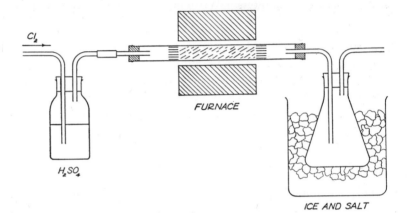

Fig. 15.   Preparation of titanium tetrachloride.

the gray porous mass with a spatula into small pieces and pack them into the combustion tube, using plugs of fibrous asbestos to hold the mass in place. The asbestos for these should be dried immediately beforehand by heating it for a few minutes to redness in a crucible. The plugs will stay in place if they are tamped down a little.

It is most important to have everything as dry as possible; therefore no time should be wasted in packing the tube with the asbestos plugs and the ignited titanium dioxide-carbon mixture. One way to make sure the contents of the combustion tube are dry is to pass dry nitrogen through the tube and heat to redness in a stream of dry nitrogen before introducing the chlorine.

Pass a slow stream of chlorine through the tube and heat it to redness. When it is red-hot and titanium chloride is being formed, pass the chlorine faster. Since the reaction is fast at a moderate red heat, the combustion-glass grade of Pyrex glass is satisfactory. This glass softens below 1000°, so it should not be heated to bright redness.

The titanium tetrachloride condenses as a liquid in the receiver and is colored yellow from dissolved chlorine. Transfer the liquid quickly to a glass-stoppered flask (which must be well dried) containing a few fine copper turnings, and leave it in contact with the copper overnight to allow the copper to react with the excess chlorine. Then decant the liquid into a small dry distilling flask, distill the liquid (b.p. 136°), and collect and store the distillate in a glass-stoppered bottle. It can be used for Experiment 51 if desired.

In handling titanium tetrachloride, remember that it fumes heavily in moist air and combines with water very vigorously. When poured into water it spatters, and care should be taken to protect the clothing.

Anhydrous titanium trichloride. Titanium trichloride can be prepared in very small yield from the tetrachloride by passing the vapor of the latter together with hydrogen through a heated tube. Bubble hydrogen through a few milliliters of titanium tetrachloride and pass the gases through a tube of Pyrex combustion glass of about 8 to 10 mm outside diameter, then through a trap cooled in ice and salt to condense the unreacted titanium tetrachloride. Lead the excess hydrogen into the draft where it will not catch fire. As soon as the air is displaced, heat the Pyrex tube very strongly to near its softening point. Titanium trichloride deposits as a dark purple sublimate just beyond the heated portion.

QUESTIONS

1. Name three other volatile chlorides that can appropriately be made by the method used here for titanium tetrachloride.

2. Name three nonmetal chlorides for which this method of preparation will not work.

3. Write equations for the various reactions which can occur between titanium tetrachloride and water.

4. Compare $TiCl_4$ with (a) $SiCl_4$, (b) $ThCl_4$.

5. Compare $TiCl_4$ with $TiCl_3$ in the light of the covalency rules.

19. Stannic Chloride and Ammonium Chlorostannate

These are good examples of a covalent chloride which becomes hydrated in solution, and of a complex salt.

(A) *Stannic chloride.* Tin and chlorine are combined directly in the apparatus shown in Fig. 16. Instead of the retort, a small Pyrex distilling flask with air condenser can be used for the reaction vessel. The apparatus must be quite dry, and must be set up in the hood.

Place 20 grams of granulated tin in the retort and turn on a slow stream of chlorine. Note that the inlet tube for the chlo-

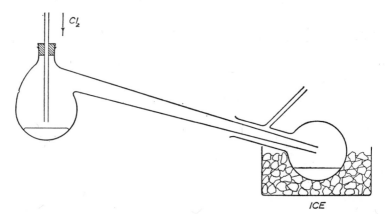

ICE

Fig. 16. Preparation of stannic chloride.

rine reaches just above the surface of the tin. If the reaction does not start right away, warm the tin gently with a Bunsen flame. Once the reaction starts, the heat of reaction keeps the tin melted. The chlorine can then be turned on faster. Stannic chloride condenses to a liquid in the receiver, which is a small distilling flask cooled in ice. When the tin is all burned (as it will be soon), shut off the chlorine, remove the receiver, and put a few pieces of tin foil into the liquid to combine with the free chlorine dissolved in it. Cork, and shake at intervals for about half an hour, or until the yellow color of the liquid has gone; then attach a condenser and thermometer and distill the stannic chloride (b.p. 114°). The yield should be nearly quantitative.

(B) *Ammonium chlorostannate.* Take your entire yield of stannic chloride, weigh it, and dissolve it in a roughly equal volume of water. (From this solution, crystals of the hydrates of stannic chloride can be obtained.) Add about a 50 per cent excess of ammonium chloride, in the form of a saturated solution, and then cool, finally cooling in ice. Filter the white crystals of ammonium chlorostannate, wash with a very little ice water, dry, and weigh.

Tests

Test a dilute solution of your product for chloride ions. Also test for stannic ions by adding ammonia and observing whether any hydrated tin dioxide is precipitated.

QUESTIONS

1. Why does stannic chloride not give a copious precipitate of tin dioxide with water, by analogy with titanium tetrachloride or antimony trichloride?

2. Why is ammonium chlorostannate called "pink salt"?

3. Compare $SnCl_4$ and $PbCl_4$.

20. Antimony Trichloride

Antimony trichloride can be prepared from stibnite, Sb_2S_3, the chief ore of antimony. The solubility of this sulfide is intermediate between those of copper sulfide and zinc sulfide, so that it can be precipitated by hydrogen sulfide from 0.3M hydrochloric acid but is easily soluble in 12M hydrochloric acid.

Heat 50 grams of stibnite in a beaker with 250 ml of concentrated hydrochloric acid in the hood until no nore hydrogen sulfide is evolved. Filter through a plug of glass wool, then evaporate the filtrate as far as possible on the steam bath; this operation takes about 2 hours. The solution must not be left on the steam bath any longer than necessary, otherwise the antimony chloride will evaporate away, even at room temperature. If any crystals appear during the evaporation, filter them out. They are probably lead chloride.

Transfer the solution to a small round-bottom flask fitted with a short fractionating column thermometer and a condenser. Since antimony trichloride attacks rubber and cork, ground-glass joints are strongly recommended. If they are not available, use corks that have been dipped in sodium silicate solution

(1 part of water glass to 1 part of water) and allowed to dry. Distill the liquid, rejecting what comes over below 210°, since this is mainly hydrochloric acid. Above 210°, antimony trichloride distills. Collect this in a dry weighed bottle. The product should be white, but if cork connections were used it will be slightly pink or brown. It melts at 73.4° when pure and is very deliquescent.

Test the behavior of antimony chloride toward water and write an equation for the reaction. Find out by experiment if this reaction is reversible.

QUESTIONS

1. Compare the reactions of antimony trichloride and phosphorus trichloride toward water.

2. Both PCl_3 and $SbCl_3$ combine reversibly with chlorine to form pentachlorides. Which should be more stable, PCl_5 or $SbCl_5$?

21. Anhydrous Ferrous and Ferric Chlorides

The object of this experiment is to prepare small specimens of anhydrous ferrous and ferric chlorides and to compare their properties. This pair of chlorides illustrates very well the rule that covalency is favored by high ionic charge, ferric chloride being much more covalent in its properties than ferrous chloride. In performing this experiment be particularly careful to record all that you observe. It is essential that the iron be clean and that the hydrogen chloride and chlorine be perfectly dry.

(A) *Ferrous chloride.* Set up the apparatus shown in Fig. 17. It is designed to pass dry hydrogen chloride gas over heated iron. About a gram of clean iron card teeth or steel wool is used and is packed into one end of a horizontal Pyrex tube about 15 mm in diameter. In the generator place 20 grams of common salt, and put concentrated sulfuric acid in the dropping funnel and in the bubbler bottle. The gas must pass through at least 10 cm of sulfuric acid for proper drying. Conduct the exit gases into the flue or absorb the hydrogen chloride in sodium hydroxide solution as in Experiment 1. Let the acid drip slowly on to the salt so that hydrogen chloride is generated. Heat the iron strongly until enough ferrous chloride has been produced to perform the necessary tests. Then let the tube cool, stop passing hydrogen chloride, disconnect the generator, and draw a stream of air through the tube by means of an aspirator to displace the hydrogen chloride.

Remove the ferrous chloride with a glass rod and dissolve some of it in a few milliliters of distilled water in a test tube. Immediately test the solution with litmus and Congo red (Congo red is blue at pH 3 and red above pH 5). Also test the solubility of ferrous chloride in ether. No yield of ferrous chloride is to be recorded, since only a part of the iron reacts.

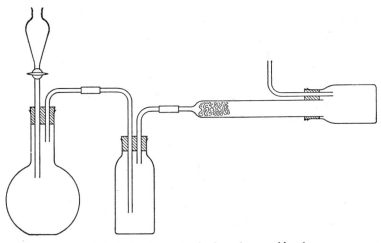

Fig. 17.   Preparation of anhydrous ferrous chloride.

(B) *Ferric chloride.* Use the same apparatus as in part A, cleaning and thoroughly drying the Pyrex tube before replacing it. In the place of the flask for generating hydrogen chloride, attach a chlorine cylinder. If no chlorine cylinder is available, the gas may be generated from potassium permanganate and concentrated hydrochloric acid, but in this case it must be dried very carefully, using a calcium chloride tube and at least two wash bottles of concentrated sulfuric acid. Weigh the receiver (the bottle on the right in the diagram), together with a cork, to 0.1 gram. In the Pyrex tube put 1.0 gram of card teeth and pack them tightly, as before. Pass a fairly rapid stream of chlorine through the apparatus and heat the iron to start the reaction. The ferric chloride is volatile enough that most of it can be made to pass into the receiver; what stays in the tube can be scraped into the receiver afterward. When no more reaction is taking place, stop passing chlorine and suck the chlorine out of the apparatus as before. Remove the receiver, quickly scrape into it the ferric chloride from the tube, stopper, and weigh. The product is very deliquescent.

Perform the same tests with ferric chloride that you did with ferrous chloride. List in tabular form all the physical and chemical properties of these two compounds that you have observed.

QUESTIONS

1. What are the main structural factors determining the boiling point of an inorganic compound? (See Pauling, *Nature of the Chemical Bond*, Chapter 2.)

2. Which should have the higher boiling point, ferric chloride or ferric fluoride?

3. How would you make anhydrous ferrous chloride in quantity, starting with metallic iron? (For a suggestion, see Experiment 3.)

4. How does anhydrous ferric chloride compare in appearance with hydrated ferric chloride?

22. Silica Gel[14]

This experiment involves periods of waiting, so it must be run concurrently with other work.

Sodium silicate reacts with acid solutions to precipitate silicon dioxide. This forms a gelatinous precipitate or a clear jelly, depending on the conditions. The jelly on drying forms glassy lumps (silica gel) that absorb water very strongly and are used as a drying agent, for example in keeping steel articles from rusting during storage.[15] Silica gel is also used to recover solvent vapors from the air, for example in dry cleaning.

A solution of sodium silicate is provided, containing 20 per cent by weight of the compound ($Na_2O + 3.36 \ SiO_2$)—actually a mixture of two or more sodium silicates having the average composition indicated by this formula. It was made by diluting water glass with an equal volume of water. Its specific gravity is 1.18. 6N sulfuric acid is also provided.

Take 100 ml of 6N sulfuric acid in a beaker of at least 400 ml

---

[14] *Inorganic Syntheses*, **2**, 95. The author is also indebted to Dr. C. Calmon, of the Permutit Company, for suggestions concerning this preparation.

[15] See *Chemical and Engineering News*, **21**, 1943, page 1054.

capacity. Stir it vigorously with a glass rod (but do not splash!) and pour in *all at once* 100 ml of sodium silicate solution. Good stirring and quick mixing are essential. Note whether there is any change in temperature immediately on mixing, and draw your conclusion about whether any reaction has taken place. After about an hour the liquid should set to a clear, firm gel. Record all that you observe.

Leave the gel to stand for 4 hours, covering the beaker with a watch glass. Then break up the gel into small lumps with a spatula and wash with at least 7 liters of water. The absorption capacity of the gel is improved if the wash water has a pH of 3.5, but for this experiment ordinary tap water can be used. The best way to wash the gel is then to put the broken gel into a 2½-liter bottle and pass in tap water by a tube leading through a two-hole stopper to the bottom of the bottle. Let the water flow out through a second tube that just passes through the stopper. Pass water at as high a speed as is possible without washing the gel out of the bottle, until the effluent no longer gives a red or orange color with the indicator thymol blue. (Since sulfuric acid was in excess, the pH of the wash water serves to indicate the completeness of the washing.) Good washing is essential to obtaining a good product.

Dry the washed gel in the oven at 150° for a few hours. Remove, cool in the desiccator over calcium chloride, and weigh immediately. Leave the preparation to stand in the air for an hour, then weigh again and record the uptake of moisture. (If the atmosphere is very dry, let the preparation stand in a second desiccator over water for an hour.)

In your account explain clearly how the theoretical yield is calculated. Compare your yield with the theoretical. You may find that your yield is apparently more than 100 per cent; explain how this result is obtained.

Sodium aluminosilicate gel. This experiment illustrates the preparation of a different type of gel. Prepare a sodium aluminate solution that is 0.5-molar in aluminum, either by dissolving powdered sodium aluminate, $NaAlO_2 \cdot H_2O$, in water and filtering or by adding sodium hydroxide solution to a solution of aluminum sulfate until the aluminum hydroxide first precipitated has just dissolved. Mix 30 ml of the 20 per cent sodium silicate solution used for silica gel with 20 ml of water in a 400-ml beaker;

swirl the liquid around, and quickly pour in 100 ml of the sodium aluminate solution.

In a few seconds a stiff gel results.   Contrast the properties of this gel with those of silica gel.

This particular gel after washing and drying can be used as a very efficient ion exchanger for water softening.   Other aluminosilicate gels can be made by mixing sodium silicate solutions with solutions of aluminum sulfate and other metallic sulfates; some of these gels containing heavy metals are dried, powdered, and used as catalysts in the fluid-flow method for petroleum cracking.

QUESTIONS

1. What changes are taking place in the mixture between the time the reactants are mixed and the time it sets to form silica gel?

2. What is meant by the term "hydrous oxide"?   Silica gel is a hydrous oxide.   How could you show experimentally that it is a hydrous oxide and not silicic acid?

23. Hydrous Oxide Sols by Ion Exchange

The common method for preparing a colloidal solution of hydrous ferric oxide, for example, has been to hydrolyze ferric chloride in solution by heat, and remove the hydrochloric acid by dialysis.   Colloidal silica can be made in a similar way, that is, by dialyzing a solution of sodium silicate.   One hydrolysis product—hydrochloric acid or sodium hydroxide—can pass through the membrane used for dialysis, whereas the colloidal particles of hydrous oxide cannot.   The process is rather tedious and takes hours or even days.   A much simpler method is to take out the acid or alkali with one of the solid ion exchangers or acid absorbers used in water purification.[16]

(A) *Hydrous ferric oxide sol.*   Here an acid-absorbing resin is used to take out the acid formed in hydrolysis of a ferric salt.   De-Acidite or Amberlite IR-4 are both excellent for the purpose.   They come in golden-brown granules of size about 10–20 mesh.   Take about 50 ml of either material in a beaker, cover with dilute hydrochloric acid, and stir; transfer to a vertical tube, 35 × 2 cm, drawn out at the bottom, with a short piece of rubber tube and screw clamp attached, as in Fig. 18.   Put a plug of glass

---

[16] J. W. Ryznar, *Ind. Eng. Chem.*, **36** (1944), 821.

wool in the bottom of the tube to support the resin. Drain out the hydrochloric acid, but in this and in the manipulations following do not let the level of liquid fall below the top of the bed of resin granules. Wash by pouring through about 250 ml of distilled water, and remove the combined hydrochloric acid from the resin by slowly passing about 250 ml of 1M ammonia. The resin is a condensation product of an amine with formaldehyde, and its combination with acids can be represented thus:

$$R_3N + H^+ + Cl^- \rightleftharpoons R_3NH^+Cl^-$$

The resin salt, as well as the resin in the basic condition, is quite insoluble in water.

Wash out the ammonia with at least 250 ml of distilled water and pass 50 ml of M/100 hydrochloric acid. Now pass a solution containing 2 grams of ferric sulfate (anhydrous) and 1 ml of 6M hydrochloric acid in a liter of water, at a flow rate of 50–100 ml per minute; this is fast enough that you can hardly count the drops at the outlet of the tube. A clear orange-red ferric oxide sol flows out of the bottom, in striking contrast to the almost colorless influent.

Tests

Test the ferric oxide sol as follows:

1. Test with litmus.
2. Test the electrical conductivity, if this is convenient.

Fig. 18. Ion exchange tube.

3. Test 10-ml portions with 1 ml of 0.1 M potassium chloride and 1 ml of 0.1M potassium sulfate, also with 0.1 ml of 0.1M potassium sulfate and 0.1 ml of 0.1M potassium citrate. You should see a marked difference in the coagulating powers of these three salts. If the proportions given do not show this difference, use more dilute or more concentrated salt solutions. The ease of coagulation increases with the age of the sol, and it is difficult to predict just how much salt will be required.

(B) *Hydrous silica sol.* Here sodium hydroxide must be removed from a sodium silicate solution, and so an acid cation exchanger must be used. "Sulfonated" coals, such as Nalcite AX or Zeo-Karb, or sulfonic acid resins, such as Amberlite IR-100, are used. After treatment with acid these have the constitution RSO_3H and will combine with sodium hydroxide thus:

$$RSO_3^-H^+ + Na^+ + OH^- \rightarrow RSO_3^-Na^+ + H_2O$$

Take about 50 ml volume of wet cation exchanger and stir with dilute hydrochloric acid; transfer to a vertical tube as in part A, and wash down with dilute hydrochloric acid. If the exchanger is new material it will probably contain iron, which must be washed out with concentrated hydrochloric acid. Rinse with 250 ml of water and then pass a sodium silicate solution containing about 1 per cent of SiO_2—say 1 volume of water glass diluted with 40 volumes of water. Reject the first 50 ml of effluent and collect the next 200 ml. Test this silica sol with litmus and by conductivity. You may not think anything is in the water, since the sol is clear and colorless (apart from a faint brown color if a sulfonated coal exchanger was used), but by evaporating on a watch glass the silica will be seen to remain as a transparent flaky film.

When the sol has been aged by standing 24 hours or more, or by heating on the steam bath for two or three hours, you can try to coagulate it with aluminum sulfate or chloride. You may not succeed, because the sol is very stable. The following test will differentiate an aged silica sol from a sodium silicate solution of equal silica content.

Prepare a "silica reagent" by mixing equal volumes of 10 per cent ammonium molybdate and 5M nitric acid. Put 1 ml of the silica sol in one tube and 1 ml of silicate solution in another; dilute both with 20 ml of water, and add 1 ml of silica reagent. Yellow silicomolybdic acid forms in both tubes, but it is much more intense in the silicate solution. A fresh silica sol cannot be distinguished from a silicate solution by this test, though their reactions to litmus are quite different.

A neutral sol of 3 per cent silica prepared in this way is liable to set to a thin gel on standing, since there is not enough electrolyte present to stabilize it. A very little sodium silicate stabilizes the sol so that it can be concentrated to 20 per cent silica content, and such a sol is used in large quantities in textile dressing.

After you have prepared these sols, wash the acid-absorbing

resin with dilute hydrochloric acid, and wash the cation exchanger first with water, then with dilute acid.

Note, again, that while using an ion exchanger bed you must never let it drain. If it accidentally does drain, the air between the granules can be removed by backwashing, that is, by passing a stream of water upwards through the bed.

QUESTIONS

1. What is meant by the term "hydrous oxide"?

2. What is the electrical charge on the particles of the ferric oxide sol?

3. Suggest two other hydrous oxide sols that can be made by this general method.

4. How is ion exchange used to remove electrolytes completely from water?

5. What is the difference in constitution between a fresh and an aged sol?

24. Nitric Oxide

Several ways are available for making nitric oxide in the laboratory, all involving the reduction of nitric or nitrous acid. The best method for making pure nitric oxide is to run 50 per cent sulfuric acid into a solution which is 4M in KNO_2 and 1M in KI.[17] This reaction proceeds in the cold, is easy to control, and gives a very pure product, but it has the drawback of expense unless the iodine is recovered. If this method is used for the preparation, the iodine may be separated off at the end of the experiment, washed with water, and used as it is for the preparation of potassium iodate in Experiment 39. Or it may be dried and resublimed (see Experiment 46) and returned to stock.

The method to be described uses cheap materials, is easy to carry out, and gives reasonably pure nitric oxide—purer than would be obtained by the reduction of dilute nitric acid with copper.

Set up in the hood the apparatus shown in Fig. 19. In the 500-ml Erlenmeyer flask put 150 ml of water and pour in, with stirring, 27 ml (0.5 mole) of concentrated sulfuric acid; add to the hot solution 125 grams (0.5 mole) of commercial ferrous sulfate hydrate ("copperas"). In the dropping funnel place 15 ml (0.2

[17] H. L. Johnston and W. F. Giauque, *J. Am. Chem. Soc*, **51** (1929), 3194.

mole) of concentrated nitric acid mixed with twice its volume of water.   Note that the top of the dropping bottle is connected by a tube to the gas delivery line, so as to equalize the pressures in the generating flask and in the dropping funnel and to make possible the smooth addition of acid.   The large bottle to be used for collecting the gas should be of at least $2\frac{1}{2}$ liters capacity, and preferably 1 gallon (3.78 liters).   It is filled to the top with water at the start of the experiment.   As the gas accumulates in this

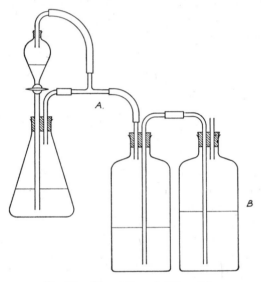

Fig. 19.   Preparation of nitric oxide.

bottle, the water is forced over into the second bottle, B, which is empty at the start of the experiment.

Disconnect the tube between the generating flask and the collecting bottle temporarily at the point marked A and heat the contents of the generating flask almost to boiling.   Run in a little nitric acid so as to generate enough nitric oxide to displace the air from the generating flask; then connect the collecting bottle to the generating flask with the rubber tube and run in the nitric acid slowly, keeping the liquid almost boiling.   Add the acid at as even a rate as possible over a period of about 15 minutes and keep the flask hot for about five minutes more, until about $2\frac{1}{2}$ to 3 liters of gas have been collected.   The nitric oxide continues to be given off for some time after the nitric acid has all been

up.   See that no lead nitrate falls between the foil and the glass.
he aluminum is not attacked during the reaction, and after-
ards the cake of lead oxide can be broken up mechanically after
aking with water.

The gas passes through an empty tube that acts as a trap, then
to a delivery tube that dips into a receiver consisting of a
ngth of 12-mm glass tubing, closed at one end and drawn down
about half its diameter at a point about 15 cm from the closed
d.   This receiver is placed in a beaker containing a freezing
xture of crushed ice and salt, well stirred together.   This

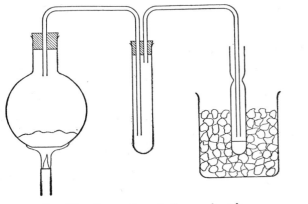

Fig. 20.   Preparation of nitrogen dioxide.

ure should freeze the nitrogen dioxide to a white solid (m.p.
°).   Since the higher oxides of nitrogen are very poisonous,
xperiment must be performed in the hood.
at the lead nitrate to decompose it; heat cautiously at first,
more strongly.   While the nitrogen dioxide is coming off,
e the effect of heat on the gas by heating, with a small
a section of one of the delivery tubes carrying the gas.
a white tile or paper behind the heated portion.   You will
e that the heat first makes the brown gas browner and then
her temperatures makes it colorless.
n all the nitrogen dioxide has been collected, remove the
r from the freezing mixture, take the delivery tube out of
let it warm up to a little below the boiling point of nitro-
xide; then seal the tube at the constriction, using a small
rch flame.   This operation calls for a little skill, since the

added.   If the heating is discontinued, gas evolution proceeds
smoothly for about 20 minutes and then starts to accelerate, and
within a minute the reaction is going so fast as to blow a lot of
reaction mixture over into the collecting flask and perhaps to
blow out one of the connections.   To avoid this, *cool the generating flask by surrounding it with cold water* as soon as you have
collected enough gas.   Close the rubber tube leading into the
collecting bottle with a screw clamp and immediately disconnect the generating flask at *A*.   For the tests to follow, the
nitric oxide is let out through *A* by opening the screw clamp; the
pressure of the water in *B* will force the gas out.   The bottle *B*
can be raised on blocks or on a stool if necessary.

Analysis.   If an Orsat analyzer is available, transfer a sample
of your gas to the analyzer and move it into a pipette containing a
concentrated acidified potassium permanganate solution.   Move
it back and forth between the absorption pipette and the measur-
ing burette some 20 times.   The gas should be completely absorbed.   It is oxidized to nitric acid.   A saturated solution of
ferrous sulfate may also be used as an absorbent.

Tests

1. Bubble the gas for a minute or two through a few milliliters of (a) ferrous sulfate solution, (b) 6M hydrochloric acid
saturated with cupric chloride, (c) ammoniacal cobalt chloride
solution.   The colored compounds formed are examples of the
very numerous complexes formed by nitric oxide and metallic
salts (see below).   In Test (a) the complex ion $(FeNO)^{++}$ is
formed.   This is an intermediate in the preparation of NO
described here.   Many of these complexes are unstable and
decompose when the solutions are heated.   Test this statement
by boiling the solutions from the above experiments.

2. Bubble nitric oxide for a few seconds through concentrated
nitric acid.

3. Collect over water a 500-ml jar of the gas and see whether it
supports the combustion of a glowing splinter.   Then put a piece
of white phosphorus in a deflagrating spoon, start it burning, and
when it is burning vigorously plunge it into the jar of gas.   The
combustion should continue.

4. Clamp horizontally a tube some 25 mm in diameter and 50
cm long; put a one-hole stopper and glass tube in one end and

connect the tube to the aspirator pump. In the other end of the tube place a two-hole stopper with two inlet tubes. Arrange to draw air in through one tube and nitric oxide through the other, first passing both the air and the nitric oxide through a few milliliters of concentrated sulfuric acid in small Erlenmeyer flasks, gas-washing bottles, or large test tubes. Put screw clamps on to the rubber connections for both the air and the nitric oxide. Turn on the aspirator so that it is sucking steadily but not too fast, and allow the air and nitric oxide to bubble at about equal rates, fairly fast, so that the bubbles can hardly be counted. The brown color that is produced in the horizontal glass tube should shade off quite noticeably from one end of the tube to the other, being lightest where the gases come in and darkest where they go out. The reaction $2NO + O_2 \rightarrow 2NO_2$ is measurably slow; its rate has been studied with some care, since it is one of the very few homogeneous termolecular reactions known. An interesting feature of termolecular reactions, which is not hard to explain, is that they do not go much faster, if at all, if the temperature is raised; the temperature coefficient of the reaction velocity is very small and may even be negative.[18]

This reaction may be used to prepare nitrogen dioxide. In this case the air must bubble more than five times as fast as the nitric oxide, the wide tube should be replaced by a large flask to allow full opportunity for reaction, and the nitrogen dioxide must be caught in a trap cooled in dry ice.

Notes on the addition reactions of nitric oxide. Nitric oxide is an "odd molecule," with an odd number of electrons. Probably because of this fact it is unusually active in forming coordination compounds. Examples of such coordination compounds and complex ions are $(FeNO)^{++}$, $[Co(NH_3)_5NO]^{++}$, $CuNOCl_3^-$, $FeNOCl_3$, $AlNOCl_3$, $Fe(CN)_5NO^=$, and the nitrosyl carbonyls, such as $Co(CO)_3NO$. Many of these complexes are unstable and decompose on heating. They appear to be formed by the donation of either one or three electrons from the NO molecule; thus in the nitroprusside ion, $Fe(CN)_5NO^=$, produced by the action of nitric acid on a ferrocyanide, the nitric oxide is considered to contribute three electrons to the iron atom, leaving the latter in the ferrous rather than the ferric condition. Likewise the existence

[18] M. Bodenstein, *Z. physikal. Chem.*, **100** (1922), 68.

of $Co(CO)_3NO$ is best understood if the NO electrons (see Experiment 13).[19]

Questions

1. What is the most important industrial method For what is nitric oxide used?

2. From your knowledge of the processes referre the reaction $2NO + O_2 \rightarrow 2NO_2$ exothermic or end

3. What would be the main advantage of usi nitrite as the source of nitrogen for this prep method you have used be adapted to use sodium material instead of nitric acid?

4. The method here given for the preparation factory for small quantities (0.1 to 0.2 mole) but preparing larger amounts. How would you prepare pure nitric oxide in, say, 2-mole quantit

25. Nitrogen Dioxide (

This substance is most easily prepared b which, like all nitrates except those of ammonium, decomposes on heating to give nitrogen dioxide. The nitrogen dioxide the oxygen by its much higher boiling poi

Calculate the weight of lead nitrate nee of nitrogen dioxide. Put this weight of dried in the oven at 150°, in a small round a cork and delivery tube as shown in Fig begun, the cork must be dipped in a s volume of water glass to 1 volume of some protection from the nitrogen di should not be used.

The molten lead monoxide produc glass and may ruin the flask if the latt putting the lead nitrate in the reaction of aluminum foil on the bottom of th the neck a circle of aluminum foil, thimble; press it out inside the flask it forms a hemispherical cup, and p

[19] An excellent summary of the react T. Moeller, *J. Chem. Educ.*, **23** (1946), 44

walls of the tube must not be drawn out too thin. The best procedure is to collapse the walls of the constricted portion by rotating the tube in the flame while the contents are still quite cold, then drawing out to give a thick-walled capillary but not actually sealing this capillary until the nitrogen dioxide has warmed up nearly to its boiling point.

Estimate the volume of liquid as closely as you can.

QUESTIONS

1. What influence have the size and charge of the cation on the stability of a metal nitrate to heat? List the following nitrates in the probable order of their ease of decomposition: calcium, barium, aluminum.

2. Why is lead nitrate more suitable than calcium nitrate for this preparation?

3. Explain the effect of temperature on the color of nitrogen dioxide.

4. Write an electronic structural formula for NO_2 and comment on any unusual feature.

5. This method is obviously unsatisfactory for preparing more than small quantities of nitrogen dioxide. How would you prepare the gas in quantities of 5 moles or more?

26. Chromium Trioxide

Chromic acid is a rather weak acid and is also unstable, losing water easily to form its anhydride, CrO_3. This oxide is extremely soluble in water, but the solubility is greatly reduced by adding sulfuric acid, as will be seen in the phase diagram in Fig. 21. It is therefore an easy matter to precipitate chromium trioxide by adding an excess of sulfuric acid to a solution of a chromate or dichromate. The difficulty comes in drying and handling the product, which is extremely hygroscopic and powerfully oxidizing.

Dissolve 30 grams (0.10 mole) of sodium dichromate, $Na_2Cr_2O_7 \cdot 2H_2O$, in 25 ml of water. Stir into the cold solution 40 grams of concentrated sulfuric acid (22 ml), adding the acid slowly as soon as the precipitate begins to appear. Let the hot solution cool to about 25° and filter the crystals on a glass or asbestos filter under suction. Use the apparatus shown in Fig. 22, which is designed to permit dry air to be sucked over the crystals to remove excess solvent. The filter is a cylindrical tube A in the bottom of which is fused a coarse sintered glass plate B, or, less desirably, a perforated porcelain or glass plate on which is laid a circle of glass filter cloth or a mat of asbestos fiber or glass wool. The tube *A* should first be weighed dry, with the filter in place and the upper end closed by a solid rubber stopper. During the filtration and drying, the tube is kept closed at the upper end by a rubber stopper which carries a tube connected to a phosphorus pentoxide drying tube *D* and a calcium chloride tower *C*, as shown in Fig. 22.

First suck the crystals as free as possible from adhering mother liquor. Then turn off the suction, pour over the crystals about 10 ml of concentrated nitric acid, and suck the acid through

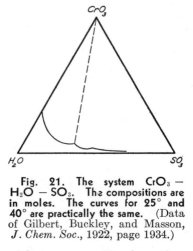

Fig. 21. The system CrO_3 — H_2O — SO_3. The compositions are in moles. The curves for 25° and 40° are practically the same. (Data of Gilbert, Buckley, and Masson, *J. Chem. Soc.*, 1922, page 1934.)

slowly. Repeat with two more 20-ml portions of concentrated nitric acid and then suck dry air through the crystals for two hours or more until the crystals are perfectly dry and loose. Quickly replace the stopper at the top of *A* with the solid stopper, and weigh the tube and contents. The difference in weight between this weighing and the weight of the empty tube gives the weight of the product.

Analysis of the product. Replace the solid stopper on *A* with a one-hole rubber stopper which carries about 15 cm of glass tubing, 5 to 7 mm in internal diameter and sealed at one end. Shake enough chromium trioxide into this tube to fill two or three centimeters of its length, remove the tube, tap the oxide down to the closed end, and in a small blowpipe flame draw the tube out in the middle and seal it. All this should be done quickly so that the material is in contact with the air as little as possible. Weigh the sealed tube containing the chromium trioxide, then break it cleanly with the aid of a file and transfer the contents quantitatively to water in a small beaker, and make up the aqueous solution to 250 ml in a volumetric flask. Also dry the pieces of the opened glass tube and weigh them, so as to get the weight of the chromium trioxide sample. Titrate 25-ml portions of the chromic acid solution in any way that seems suitable. For

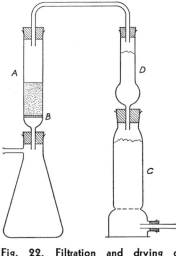

Fig. 22. Filtration and drying of chromium trioxide.

example, to the chromic acid solution add dilute sulfuric acid and a gram of potassium iodide, and immediately titrate the liberated iodine with 0.1N sodium thiosulfate. Calculate the percentage purity of your chromium trioxide. It will probably be about 90 per cent, the impurity being water.

QUESTIONS

1. Why is sodium dichromate used in this preparation, rather than potassium dichromate?

2. How would you prepare a sample of really dry chromium trioxide, of purity good enough for an atomic-weight determination?

3. Would it be permissible to wash the chromium trioxide with alcohol and ether to dry it?

4. Compare chromium trioxide with sulfur trioxide.

27. Sodium Peroxyborate

This preparation, illustrating the formation of the salt of a peroxyacid from hydrogen peroxide, is to be compared with Experiment 48, where the peroxysalt is formed electrolytically.

Prepare a solution of sodium metaborate, $NaBO_2$, by dissolving 19 grams (0.05 mole) of borax, $Na_2B_4O_7 \cdot 10H_2O$, and 4 grams (0.10 mole) of sodium hydroxide in 120 ml of warm water. Cool, add slowly 23 ml of 30 per cent hydrogen peroxide diluted with 50 ml of water (230 ml of 3 per cent hydrogen peroxide can be used), and cool in ice. Stir for about 15 minutes, or until the crystallization of sodium peroxyborate appears to be complete. Filter the crystals under suction, wash with alcohol and ether, and dry. The product is $NaBO_3 \cdot 4H_2O$.

Tests

To portions of sodium peroxyborate solution add the following reagents:

(1) Dilute sulfuric acid and potassium permanganate.
(2) Dilute sulfuric acid and potassium iodide.
(3) Titanium sulfate solution (Experiment 28).
(4) Litmus paper.
Repeat these tests with hydrogen peroxide solution.

QUESTIONS

1. If the solution of sodium metaborate prepared in this experiment is evaporated, borax will crystallize out. Explain.

2. A solution of borax in water is quite strongly alkaline. Explain, therefore, why borax can be regarded as an acid salt.

3. How would you attempt to prepare solid $NaBO_2$?

4. Write a structural formula for sodium peroxyborate and compare it with the formula of perchloric acid.

(*Other questions on peroxyacids and peroxides are asked after Experiments 28 and 48.*)

28. Titanic Sulfate Solution: Hydrogen Peroxide Tests

Titanic sulfate. Titanium dioxide as usually obtained is practically insoluble in sulfuric acid, concentrated or dilute. One of the few ways to get it into solution is bisulfate fusion.

Take 5 grams of potassium acid sulfate, $KHSO_4$, and heat gently in an uncovered porcelain crucible until most of the frothing has ceased and potassium pyrosulfate, $K_2S_2O_7$, remains. Add 0.5 gram of finely powdered titanium dioxide and heat to fusion. Keep the crucible red-hot for 15 minutes, with the cover on to keep in the heat. Then cool, rocking the contents of the crucible gently with the aid of tongs so that they solidify as a film around the sides of the crucible rather than as a lump in the bottom. When the crucible is quite cold, place it in a beaker with 100 cc of cold 1M sulfuric acid, and leave to stand, with occasional stirring, until the contents of the crucible have dissolved. You now have a solution containing titanic sulfate, probably with the ion TiO^{++}.

Test for hydrogen peroxide. Add a little titanic sulfate solution to some 3 per cent hydrogen peroxide. The yellow color is due to peroxytitanic acid, probably H_2TiO_4, and is very intense, as will be seen. Mix 1 ml of 3 per cent hydrogen peroxide with 100 ml of water; this solution is 0.03 per cent, or 300 parts per million (p.p.m.). Pour 10 ml of this solution into one test tube and 1 ml into a second test tube, add 9 ml of water, and mix. Dilute twice more until you have four test tubes, containing hydrogen peroxide of concentrations 300 p.p.m., 30 p.p.m., 3 p.p.m., and 0.3 p.p.m. To each tube add 1 ml of titanic sulfate solution. Estimate the lowest concentration of hydrogen peroxide detectible by this test.

The colored compound is quite stable and obeys Beer's Law making it possible to use the reaction for the colorimetric determination of hydrogen peroxide and of titanium.

Peroxides and dioxides. To show the difference between peroxides, which are salts of hydrogen peroxide and yield hydrogen peroxide on treatment with acids, and dioxides, which merely contain a metal in its +4 oxidation state, take small amounts of BaO_2, MnO_2, PbO_2, and Na_2O_2 in test tubes, add 10 ml of ice-cold dilute sulfuric acid to each, shake for a minute, let the solids settle, and add titanic sulfate solution to each tube. Note whether or not a yellow color is produced.

Peroxyacids and peracids. Test cold solutions of sodium peroxyborate, potassium or ammonium peroxydisulfate, and potassium perchlorate with dilute sulfuric acid and titanic sulfate. If you have not already done so, perform Test 2 of Experiment 48 (on peroxymonosulfuric acid).

QUESTIONS

1. Write structural formulas for the oxides tested in this experiment, and show how the structures explain the reactions.

2. Do the same for the oxyacids (peroxyboric, and so on) tested in this experiment.

3. Name four metals that form colored compounds with hydrogen peroxide as titanium does.

4. Which of these metals can be determined colorimetrically by their hydrogen peroxide reaction?

5. What is the commercial method of making hydrogen peroxide?

29. Phosphates of Sodium[20]

The object of this experiment is to prepare small samples of some of the various sodium phosphates and to compare their properties.

The oxyacids of pentavalent phosphorus are surprisingly numerous, and their chemistry is very complex. These considerations have only begun to be appreciated in recent years, when research has been stimulated by the discovery of important applications for the salts of these acids. The main application of the soluble phosphates is in water conditioning. Many of them possess the property of combining with calcium and magnesium ions to form extremely stable soluble complexes that do not give precipitates with soap and do not deposit scale in boilers. Similar complexes are formed with iron, and stable soluble phosphates of iron find application in nutrition. Other uses for soluble phosphates are found in the textile industry, paints, and insecticide sprays.

The starting point in the preparation of the phosphates is orthophosphoric acid, H_3PO_4, obtained by the reaction of phosphorus pentoxide and excess of water. Orthophosphoric acid, being tribasic, forms three series of salts, the sodium salts being

[20] A very thorough account of the phosphates, with literature references, is given in Yost and Russell, *Systematic Inorganic Chemistry*, Chapter 6.

For properties and applications, see the symposium in *Industrial and Engineering Chemistry*, **34** (1942), 9–52.

For sodium tripolyphosphate see H. Huber, *Z. Angew. Chem.*, **50** (1936), 323.

NaH_2PO_4, Na_2HPO_4, and Na_3PO_4. When the first two salts are heated to redness, they lose water (as do all acid salts of oxyacids), yielding sodium metaphosphate, $NaPO_3$, and sodium pyrophosphate, $Na_4P_2O_7$, respectively. The empirical formula $NaPO_3$ represents at least four different substances with varying degrees of polymerization; the highest polymer of known composition is the hexametaphosphate, $Na_6P_6O_{18}$, sold commercially as Calgon for its remarkable water-softening properties. Calgon solutions, however, also contain colloidal matter of high but unknown molecular weight.

If sodium metaphosphate and sodium pyrophosphate are heated together under the right conditions, sodium tripolyphosphate, $Na_5P_3O_{10}$, is formed, which also forms complex ions with calcium and magnesium. For binding calcium ions, sodium tripolyphosphate is not so good as the hexametaphosphate but is better than the pyrophosphate. For binding magnesium ions, pyrophosphate is best and tripolyphosphate second best.

Two sodium metaphosphates, the pyrophosphate, and the tripolyphosphate are prepared in this exercise. The sodium "hexametaphosphate" is an amorphous glass and cannot be recrystallized from solution; the other three products could be crystallized if desired, but in this exercise only the properties of their solutions are studied.

In aqueous solution, all these salts are eventually converted into salts of orthophosphoric acid, but the conversion is rapid only with the dimetaphosphate. Most of the solutions can be kept for a week without appreciable change so long as they are kept cold and are not acid. On boiling with acid they are converted to orthophosphates within a few hours.

Sodium hexametaphosphate, $(NaPO_3)_6$. Weigh a small platinum crucible to the nearest centigram, put in about seven grams of crystalline sodium acid phosphate, $NaH_2PO_4 \cdot H_2O$, and weigh again. Then heat over a Meker burner to a bright red heat, continuing to heat for 10 or 15 minutes after the last effervescence has ceased. Remove the flame and, holding the crucible with a pair of tongs, swirl the contents round so that they solidify in a thin layer around the walls; then complete the cooling by cautiously dipping the bottom of the crucible in a dish of water. Rapid cooling is necessary to get the desired product.

Weigh again when the crucible is cold and dissolve the salt in warm water (50°) in a small beaker. As soon as it has all dissolved, transfer the solution to a 100-ml volumetric flask, cool, make up to the mark with water, and mix up the solution thoroughly. Use this solution for the tests described below.

Sodium hexametaphosphate prepared in this manner is sold under the trade name Calgon for use as a detergent and water softener.

Sodium pyrophosphate, $Na_4P_2O_7$. Weigh out in the platinum crucible, to the nearest centigram, about seven grams of crystalline disodium phosphate, $Na_2HPO_4 \cdot 7H_2O \cdot$ (Take more than seven grams if the crucible is big enough, but the crucible must not be more than half full.) Heat over a Meker burner, cautiously at first because of the considerable frothing due to loss of water, but finally heat to bright redness for 10 minutes as before. You will probably have to put a cover over the crucible to get a high enough temperature to melt the salt (m.p. 988°). Cool rapidly. The rate of cooling does not affect the chemical nature of this product, but faster cooling gives smaller crystals that dissolve more easily. Weigh the crucible and contents when cool; then dissolve in water and make up to 100 ml in a volumetric flask as before. Set this solution aside too.

The next two salts to be described take longer to prepare, and it will usually be best to make the tests on the first two solutions while the second two salts are being prepared. However, the remaining preparations will be described next and the tests afterward.

Sodium dimetaphosphate, $(NaPO_3)_2$. Weigh out in the platinum crucible about seven grams of sodium acid phosphate and heat as described under sodium hexametaphosphate, again cooling quickly. The sodium hexametaphosphate is now "annealed" by heating the crucible on a sand bath over a small flame for 6 hours. Cover the crucible with a piece of aluminum foil with a round hole cut in it with a cork borer, just large enough to admit a thermometer, which is suspended so that its bulb rests on the solid mass of hexametaphosphate. Heap the sand around the sides of the crucible to give more uniform heating, and keep the temperature at 260° to 280° for 6 hours. Then cool and dissolve in cold water, making the volume up to 100 ml as previously.

Since this salt hydrolyzes rather rapidly in solution to pyrophosphate, the tests should be made upon it as soon as possible.

Sodium tripolyphosphate, $Na_5P_3O_{10}$. Since this salt must also be "annealed," it is a good plan to perform this preparation in a second platinum crucible, annealing on the same sand bath and at the same time as the sodium dimetaphosphate.

From the weights of starting material and product recorded in the first two preparations, calculate the weights of sodium dihydrogen phosphate and disodium hydrogen phosphate to give about five grams of a product in which $NaPO_3$ and $Na_4P_2O_7$ will be in a ratio of formula weights 1:1, or 1 gram of $NaPO_3$ to 2.62 grams of $Na_4P_2O_7$. Note that the weights of crystalline sodium dihydrogen phosphate and disodium hydrogen phosphate to be taken cannot be calculated from the molecular weights of their hydrates, because these hydrates usually lose an indefinite quantity of water on storage. Moreover, Na_2HPO_4 has two common hydrates, with $7H_2O$ and $12H_2O$. Stocks of these phosphates must always be assayed, by heating weighed amounts to redness and determining the weights of the residues, before they can be used for any quantitative work.

Weigh out to the nearest centigram the amounts of the two salts required, mix thoroughly on a piece of paper, and place in the platinum crucible. Heat cautiously over the Meker burner flame, until the frothing has ceased and then to bright redness, so that the mass is completely liquid. A cover over the crucible will probably be needed. Continue to heat the fused mass for 15 minutes, then cool quickly, first swirling the molten mass around the sides of the crucible as it solidifies.

Heat the product to 260°–280° for 6 hours as described in the preceding section. During this "annealing," a reaction in the solid phase takes place; the mixture of pyrophosphate and metaphosphate is transformed to a single salt, sodium tripolyphosphate. If the molten mass is cooled quickly, the individual particles of pyrophosphate and metaphosphate are very small and intimately mixed, so that the solid phase reaction proceeds relatively quickly; but if the melt is cooled slowly, considerable segregation of the two salts takes place and the solid-phase reaction hardly has a chance.

Dissolve the mass of tripolyphosphate in cold water and make up to 100 ml in a volumetric flask.

Tests

(A) *Titration with calcium chloride.* As was indicated above, these phosphates are widely used in laundry operation and in soap powders, to prevent the calcium and magnesium ions of hard water from giving a precipitate with the soap. The value of a particular phosphate for this purpose depends not only on the amount of calcium or magnesium the phosphate can take up to form a complex ion but also on the stability of this complex. In the procedure to be described, the amount of calcium salt needed to destroy a lather of soap and water containing phosphate is measured. This procedure gives an estimate of the calcium-binding power of the phosphate for this particular application.

Prepare an 0.1M calcium chloride solution, also a standard soap solution. For the latter, an 0.04M solution of potassium palmitate is highly satisfactory. It can be made by dissolving the required amount of pure palmitic acid in *n*-propyl alcohol, adding somewhat less than its equivalent of potassium hydroxide dissolved in *n*-propyl alcohol, adding to the solution an equal volume of water and a little phenolphthalein, and completing the neutralization with aqueous potassium hydroxide until the phenophthalein is just turned pink. The solution when ready should contain about equal amounts of water and *n*-propyl alcohol.

Place 50 ml of hot distilled water in a 250-ml glass-stoppered Pyrex Erlenmeyer flask and add 5.0 ml of the soap solution. With the temperature between 60 and 90°, titrate with the 0.1M calcium chloride, stoppering the flask and shaking between drops, until the soap no longer forms a lather. If the lather disappears completely from the surface of the water within five seconds after shaking is stopped, it may be considered that the lathering power is destroyed. Repeat two or three times until you have consistent titrations. This volume of calcium chloride is the soap blank, to be subtracted from the subsequent titration volumes.

To titrate the various phosphate solutions, place 50 ml of water in the flask, heat nearly to boiling, and quickly add 5.0 ml of soap solution and 10.0 ml of phosphate solution from a pipette. Titrate immediately with calcium chloride, stoppering the flask and shaking between additions, until a stable lather is no longer formed.

Subtract the soap blank from the titration volume with each of the four phosphate solutions, and express the data in millimoles of calcium chloride per gram of phosphate and in moles of calcium chloride per formula weight of phosphate. Do your results indicate whether sodium tripolyphosphate is a chemical individual or a mixture of meta- and pyrophosphates?

(B) *Miscellaneous tests.* Perform these tests with small samples of each of the four solutions above, and also with solutions of sodium dihydrogen phosphate and disodium hydrogen phosphate. Present the results in the form of a table to show the result of each test with each phosphate.

1. Test the pH, roughly, with indicators or with a universal indicator paper such as Hydrion.

2. Add 0.1M $CaCl_2$ a few drops at a time, with shaking.

3. Add 0.1M $Fe_2(SO_4)_3$ a few drops at a time, with shaking.

3a. Where clear solutions are obtained in (3), test them with potassium thiocyanate solution to see if they contain appreciable amounts of free ferric ion.

4. Add 0.1M $AgNO_3$.

5. Add 0.1M zinc acetate plus dilute acetic acid.

6. Add an equal volume of a solution containing 50 grams of ammonium molybdate and 3 moles of nitric acid per liter, and allow to stand in the cold for a few minutes.

QUESTIONS

1. How would you prepare pure pyrophosphoric acid from sodium pyrophosphate?

2. Many supposed polyphosphates, such as $Na_6P_4O_{13}$, have been reported in the literature and afterward found to be mixtures and not chemical individuals. By what methods can the existence or nonexistence of such "compounds" be established?

30. Sulfamic Acid[21]

Sulfamic acid, or amine sulfonic acid, $SO_2(NH_2)OH$, has become an industrial chemical. Its importance is that it is one of the very few strong monobasic acids, the only other common ones being hydrochloric, nitric, and perchloric acids. Some of the salts of sulfamic acid are unusually soluble, for example these of high-molecular-weight amines. Other sulfamates have valu-

[21] *References:* P. Baumgarten, *Berichte*, **69** (1936), 1929; M. E. Cupery. *Ind. Eng. Chem.*, **30** (1938), 627 and **34** (1942), 792.

able properties, thus the ammonium salt is used in fireproofing and as a weed killer. The acid itself is solid and nonhygroscopic, and is easily obtained in great purity. For these reasons it has been recommended as a primary standard in volumetric analysis.

The constitution of the acid can be seen from its synthesis from sulfur dioxide and hydroxylamine salts. It is most easily prepared, however, from fuming sulfuric acid and urea.

Dissolve 30 grams of urea in 50 ml of concentrated sulfuric acid, cooling in an ice bath and stirring with a thermometer. To the clear solution add slowly 75 ml of 60 per cent fuming sulfuric acid, at no time letting the temperature rise above 40 or 45°. (*Warning:* Fuming sulfuric acid must be handled with care, and in the hood.) Now pour a little of this solution into a 600-ml beaker and warm on the steam bath. At about 80° a vigorous reaction occurs, with much foaming and evolution of carbon dioxide. Keep adding the solution a little at a time to the warmed beaker. When all has been added and has reacted, cool to room temperature and filter under suction on a glass, asbestos, or Vinyon filter cloth. Wash the crystals of sulfamic acid with a few milliliters of cold 70 to 80 per cent sulfuric acid, and suck them as dry as possible. The yield of crude acid should be over 90 per cent.

The product is contaminated with a little sulfuric acid and is to be recrystallized from warm water. This must be done with care, since sulfamic acid is hydrolyzed slowly by hot water. Measure out 250 ml of distilled water and heat to 75 or 80° (not higher) and add the whole preparation of crude sulfamic acid, stirring until it has all dissolved. Cool to room temperature and then cool in ice. Filter, then dry and weigh the crystals. The solubility of sulfamic acid in water at 0° is 14.68 grams per 100 grams of water; calculate the weight of sulfamic acid dissolved in the water at 0°, add this to the weight of your product, and compare the total yield with the theoretical.

The reactions in this preparation are rather complex, and the equations are therefore given here:

$$CO(NH_2)_2 + SO_3 \rightarrow NH_2 \cdot CO \cdot NH \cdot SO_3H$$
$$NH_2CO \cdot NH \cdot SO_3H + H_2SO_4 \rightarrow HO \cdot CO \cdot NH \cdot SO_3H + SO_2(NH_2)OH$$
$$HO \cdot CO \cdot NH \cdot SO_3H \rightarrow CO_2 + SO_2(NH_2)OH$$

Reactions of sulfamic acid.

1. Determine the purity of your product by weighing out accurately two samples of about 2.5 millimoles and titrating with the standard decinormal base provided, using methyl red as indicator.

2. Dissolve about a gram of the acid in 20 ml of water and divide the solution into two parts. Boil one portion for about a minute, then cool, and add barium chloride solution to both portions. Explain your observations, writing an equation for the hydrolysis of sulfamic acid.

3. Dissolve about two grams of acid in 10 ml of water, drop in a small piece of litmus paper, and add concentrated ammonia until the litmus just turns blue. Dip one or two pieces of filter paper into the solution, so that about half of the paper is wetted by the solution, then let them dry. Hold the paper at the impregnated end and light the paper at the untreated end.

4. Put about two grams of sulfamic acid and 10 to 15 ml of concentrated nitric acid into a large test tube and warm gently until gas evolution begins. Test the gas with a glowing wood splinter. Note carefully all you observe, and write equations for all reactions. The nitric acid should preferably be yellow brown at the start. You will then observe that the sulfamic acid decolorizes it even before the mixture is heated; explain.

QUESTIONS

1. If sulfamic acid had been a weak acid, would methyl red have been a good indicator for the titration?

2. What causes the evolution of heat when urea is dissolved in sulfuric acid?

3. How is fuming sulfuric acid made? Are there any salts corresponding to fuming sulfuric acid?

4. Calculate the number of moles of sulfur trioxide that you added in the form of fuming sulfuric acid in this preparation. The data needed for this calculation will be found on the bottle of fuming sulfuric acid.

5. Give two methods for preparing nitrous oxide, N_2O.

31. Lead Tetraacetate[22]

Lead tetraacetate is characteristic of the covalent compounds of tetrapositive lead. Relatively few compounds of tetrapositive lead are known, and only those with bonds having a strong covalent character are at all stable. Most of these are strong oxidizing agents. Lead tetraacetate, a strong oxidizing agent, is of value in preparative organic chemistry in that it is selective in its action, splitting glycols with the formation of two molecules of ketone or aldehyde while leaving other oxidizable groups, for example the aldehyde groups, untouched.

In preparing lead tetraacetate we could employ lead dioxide, PbO_2, as a source of tetrapositive lead. In the reaction to be described, PbO_2 is inconvenient to use because it goes into solution too slowly. Red lead, Pb_3O_4, is used instead. Red lead can be regarded as a compound of one molecule of PbO_2 with two of PbO and is made to react with acetic acid containing acetic anhydride, the function of the latter being to remove the water formed in the primary reaction:

$$Pb_3O_4 + 8CH_3COOH \rightarrow (CH_3COO)_4Pb$$
$$+ 2(CH_3COO)_2Pb + 4H_2O$$
$$4H_2O + 4(CH_3CO)_2O \rightarrow 8CH_3COOH$$

Set up a 1-liter three-necked flask with a mercury-seal stirrer and a thermometer. The mercury seal is to keep the moisture of the air out of the flask; it can be replaced by a device like that shown in Fig. 23, where a sleeve cut from a piece of rubber tubing rotates in loose contact with a glass tube lubricated with vaseline. Support the flask on a wire gauze, so that it can be heated.

Place a mixture of 550 ml of glacial acetic acid and 170 ml of acetic anhydride in the flask, and warm to 40°. Through the third neck of the flask, add slowly 300 grams of red lead that has been previously dried in an oven at 200° and cooled in a desiccator. Stir vigorously. The reaction develops heat, and the temperature must be kept below 65° by cooling the flask if necessary. Toward the end of the red lead addition, the heat of reaction no longer maintains the temperature, and the flask must be heated again to make the red lead react fast enough; but do not heat above 65°.

[22] *Inorganic Syntheses*, **1**, 47. O. Dimroth and R. Schweitzer, *Ber.*, **56** (1923), 1375.

When all has reacted, cool, decant away as much liquid as possible, and filter the lead tetraacetate crystals on a large Büchner funnel. To protect the product from undue contact with moist air, cover the funnel with a tile or piece of cardboard during filtration, which is rather slow. Wash the solid with cold glacial acetic acid. The yield is about 150 grams. It should be white but may be slightly pink or brown due to the presence of PBO_2. If a purer product is desired, it can be re-crystallized from hot glacial acetic acid. It is inter-esting to note that in the polar solvent, acetic acid, the covalent lead tetraacetate is considerably less soluble than the more ionic diacetate. In non-polar solvents like benzene this solubility order is reversed, as will be seen in Test 2 below.

A further yield of product can be obtained from the mother liquor from the preparation by heating it to 80°C with stirring, then passing in dry chlorine until no more white precipitate of lead chloride appears. The solution is filtered while hot, best through a fluted filter paper. When the filtrate is cooled, impure lead tetraacetate separates out. The above preparation may be modified by dis-pensing with the acetic anhydride entirely. Ordi-nary glacial acetic acid is used, the stirring is extremely vigorous, and the temperature is kept below 60° (Dimroth and Schweitzer, reference 22). Careful temperature control is especially important in this case, since lead tetraacetate is hydrolyzed at higher temperatures by the water formed in the reaction. When acetic anhydride is used, tempera-ture control is still necessary because lead tetraacetate oxidizes acetic anhydride above 65°–70°.

Fig. 23. Substitute for a mercury seal stirrer. The lower end of the lower rub-ber sleeve is lubricated with vaseline.

Lead tetraacetate is sensitive to moisture and soon turns brown unless it is dried carefully and kept in a tightly stoppered bottle. It is rather hard to free the crystals completely from acetic acid without causing some decomposition.

Tests

1. Add a little lead tetraacetate to water.

2. Test the solubility of lead tetraacetate in dry carbon tetrachloride or benzene.

3. Saturate 10 ml of ice-cold concentrated hydrochloric acid with lead tetraacetate, then stir in 3 grams of solid ammonium chloride. Compare the result with that of Experiment 8.

QUESTIONS

1. Suggest a way of making pure lead tetraacetate from lead diacetate without using chlorine.

2. What compound of tetrapositive lead is of great importance in industry, and how is it made?

3. What is the reaction between red lead and dilute nitric acid?

4. Devise and perform tests to show the power of lead tetraacetate to oxidize inorganic and organic compounds.

32. Lead Thiocyanate and Thiocyanogen

This preparation is of interest for the behavior of thiocyanogen, $(CNS)_2$, as a pseudohalogen. Another pseudohalogen is cyanogen, C_2N_2. These can displace halogens and be displaced by them, and have other reactions in common with the halogens, such as the formation of inter-halogen compounds (compare ICl with ICN and ICNS), the reactions with alkalies (compare Cl_2 and C_2N_2 in their reactions with cold aqueous sodium hydroxide), and addition to carbon-carbon double bonds.

Lead thiocyanate. Dissolve 33 grams (0.1 mole) of pure lead nitrate in 75 ml. of hot distilled water. Also dissolve 10 grams of potassium thiocyanate in another 75 ml of hot water. Mix the two solutions and cool, finally cooling in ice. $Pb(CNS)_2$ separates in needle-shaped crystals, which are filtered, washed with ice water, and dried in a dessicator. They are somewhat light-sensitive.

Thiocyanogen solution. In the manipulations to follow, it must be remembered that thiocyanogen is hydrolyzed rapidly with water, and all vessels and solvents must be absolutely dry.

Prepare a solution of bromine in dried redistilled ether, containing 8 grams of bromine in 250 ml of ether. Suspend 5 grams of lead thiocyanate in 50 ml of dry ether in a glass-stoppered 250-cc Erlenmeyer flask; add the bromine solution some 5 ml at a time, shaking vigorously between additions, until some 70 ml has been added. While the lead thiocyanate is reacting, the orange-red color of the bromine changes to the much lighter yellow color of thiocyanogen.

Tests

1. To a little thiocyanogen solution add a little concentrated aqueous potassium iodide and shake. Note that thiocyanogen is intermediate in activity between bromine and iodine.

2. Take 0.5 ml of an unsaturated oil such as cottonseed oil or oleic acid, place in a small dry glass-stoppered Erlenmeyer flask, and add 10 to 15 ml of your thiocyanogen solution. Shake thoroughly and leave to stand in a dark place for half an hour. Note the disappearance of the thiocyanogen color. Add a little concentrated aqueous potassium iodide; little if any iodine will be liberated.[23]

3. Shake portions of thiocyanogen solution with finely powdered iron and with mercury. Compare the action with that of a halogen.

QUESTIONS

1. The solubility of lead thiocyanate in water is much less than in the potassium nitrate solution resulting from the preparation used here. Explain.

2. Would lead acetate be as good as lead nitrate for the preparation?

3. Write an equation for the reaction between C_2N_2 and cold dilute sodium hydroxide solution. Can $(CNS)_2$ react in the same way?

4. Does $(CNO)_2$ exist? What is the probable structure of $(CNS)_2$?

33. Lead Dioxide

Lead dioxide may be made by the oxidation of plumbous hydroxide in alkaline solution. A convenient oxidizing agent is sodium or calcium hypochlorite.

Prepare a hypochlorite solution by adding 150 ml of water to 50 grams of bleaching powder having 15 per cent available chlorine or a proportional amount of bleaching powder with higher available chlorine, mixing well and filtering. Also mix

[23] For the determination of the thiocyanogen number of fats and oils, see G. S. Jamieson, *Vegetable Fats and Oils*. New York: Reinhold Publishing Corporation, 1943, page 397.

solutions of 19 grams of lead acetate [$Pb(CH_3COO)_2 \cdot 3H_2O$] in 50 ml of water and 10 grams of sodium hydroxide in 90 ml of water, adding the lead acetate to the sodium hydroxide with stirring. Now pour 80 ml of the hypochlorite solution slowly and with constant stirring into the lead acetate-sodium hydroxide mixture, heat nearly to boiling, and test a portion of the solution for complete oxidation by filtering and adding a little hypochlorite. If more brown precipitate forms, return the test solution to the main quantity and add about 10 ml more hypochlorite. Test again after a minute or two. Continue adding hypochlorite solution until no more brown precipitate forms.

Let the precipitate settle, and wash two or three times by decantation. Then stir it with 50 ml 3N nitric acid to decompose plumbates and dissolve any plumbous hydroxide. Heat nearly to boiling and wash with hot water, first by decantation and then on the Büchner funnel. Suck it as dry as possible and complete the drying in the desiccator or on the steam bath. The yield should be about 85 per cent.

To determine the purity of the product, dry a sample in a desiccator over concentrated sulfuric acid for 24 hours; then weigh out 0.5 gram and add to it 15 ml of 1:1 nitric acid and exactly 20 ml of 1 per cent hydrogen peroxide. Stir until all the product has dissolved, adding 100 ml of warm water if necessary. Titrate the excess of hydrogen peroxide with 0.1N potassium permanganate, and compare with a blank titration made with 20 ml of the 1 per cent hydrogen peroxide alone, with no lead dioxide. The product should be about 95 per cent PbO_2.

Tests

1. Heat a portion in a dry test tube.
2. Treat a portion with ice-cold concentrated hydrochloric acid and then warm the mixture.
3. Shake about a gram with a solution of manganous sulfate acidified with dilute sulfuric acid.

QUESTIONS

1. What is meant by the term "available chlorine" in bleaching powder?
2. What is the function of the sodium hydroxide?
3. What would be another way of making lead dioxide?

4. Which is the better oxidizing agent, lead dioxide or tin dioxide?
5. Which oxide is more acidic, lead dioxide or lead monoxide?
6. Compare lead dioxide and barium dioxide in constitution and properties.

34. Arsenic Acid

This preparation illustrates a general method for making an oxyacid of a nonmetal or pseudo metal, that is, the oxidation of the element or its lower oxide by concentrated nitric acid. The element arsenic could be used to make arsenic acid, but arsenious oxide is more readily available and will be used instead.

Mix 25 grams of finely powdered arsenious oxide and 75 ml of concentrated nitric acid in a beaker in the hood, and warm over a wire gauze. Brown oxides of nitrogen, which are poisonous and corrosive, are given off in large quantities. When the reaction ceases, add another 25 ml of nitric acid, stir with a glass rod if necessary to wet any unreacted solid, and continue to heat until no more brown gas comes off and a clear solution remains. If the reaction stops before all the arsenious oxide is dissolved—signified by the absence of any brown fumes—add a few drops of concentrated hydrochloric acid, which catalyzes the reaction and also produces a little arsenic trichloride. Since this is volatile and highly poisonous, see that the hood is working properly.

Transfer the clear solution to an evaporating dish and boil it down until a thick sirupy liquid is left. Cool in ice and try to make the arsenic acid crystallize by stirring in one or two crystals of a previous preparation of arsenic acid. Alternatively, dip a glass stirring rod in the liquid, take it out and evaporate the adhering solution by waving the rod over a flame; let the rod cool until a solid incrustation appears. Use this incrustation for your seed crystal. (The solid will not work if it is arsenic pentoxide instead of arsenic acid.) If no crystals can be obtained, evaporate further and try again. The crystals should have the composition $As_2O_5 \cdot 4H_2O$. Dry the crystals in a desiccator over concentrated sulfuric acid.

The brown gas given off when nitric acid and arsenious oxide are heated together is an equimolar mixture of NO_2 and NO. It can be condensed in an ice and salt freezing mixture to a blue liquid, which is N_2O_3, the anhydride of nitrous acid. This is one of the best ways of preparing N_2O_3.

Tests

Dissolve two or three grams of arsenic acid in 25 ml of hot water, divide the solution into three approximately equal portions, and test as follows:

1. Pass hydrogen sulfide or add hydrogen sulfide water, boiling for a minute or so.

2. Add silver nitrate solution and neutralize carefully with 6M ammonia, remembering that excess of ammonia will dissolve any precipitate.

3. Add 10 ml of 10 per cent ammonium molybdate and 10 ml of concentrated nitric acid, and boil the mixture in a small beaker for about 10 minutes.

Make parallel tests with a solution of orthophosphoric acid, and perform Tests 1 and 2 with a solution of arsenious acid, made by boiling arsenious oxide with water and filtering. Write equations for all reactions observed.

QUESTIONS

1. List as many examples as you can of oxides or acids that can be made by heating an element with concentrated nitric acid.

2. Compare arsenic acid with phosphoric acid with regard to (a) acid strength, (b) reducibility.

3. How do the oxidizing powers of arsenic and antimonic acids compare?

4. Suggest an easy way of making sodium arsenate from arsenious oxide which would not involve oxidation with nitric acid.

5. Iodide ion reduces arsenic acid to arsenious, yet sodium arsenite can be quantitatively oxidized to sodium arsenate by iodine in neutral solution. Explain, using an equation.

6. What is a heteropolyacid? Give five examples, including the two whose ammonium salts you prepared in this exercise.

35. Potassium Dichromate from Chromite

Chromite, $FeCr_2O_4$, is the principal ore of chromium. Chromates and dichromates are obtained from it by fusion with sodium or potassium carbonate with access of air; the iron is oxidized from the ferrous to the ferric condition and the chromium from oxidation state $+3$ to $+6$. The melt is taken up with water, sulfuric acid is added, and the dichromate is separated by a rather complicated fractional crystallization process which is a good example of the use of phase diagrams.[24]

The procedure which follows is adapted to the small scale of the laboratory. Potassium nitrate is added in the fusion to hasten oxidation, and the chromate is separated from the solution of the melt by precipitation instead of by fractional crystallization.

In an iron dish place 20 grams of potassium carbonate, 20 grams of potassium hydroxide, and 10 grams of potassium nitrate. Support the dish on a piece of asbestos board with a hole cut to fit it, and heat with a Meker burner until the mixture is melted. Then add 20 grams of finely powdered chromite, a little at a time, stirring with a stiff iron wire or the end of an old file. Heat as much as is necessary to keep the mass fluid. Effervescence occurs as the mineral is added. When all the chromite has been added, heat as strongly as possible for 20 minutes, stirring occasionally, and then cool. While the dish and contents are still hot but not so hot that undue spattering is caused, place the dish in a large evaporating dish containing enough water to cover it, and boil until all the material in the dish has been loosened. After a few minutes' boiling the solution should be bright yellow. If it is still green after 10 minutes' boiling, add a little hydrogen peroxide. Then filter, washing the residue on the filter paper with hot water. What is this residue?

Evaporate the combined filtrate and washings, which contain the chromate, to 100 to 150 ml. Add 1:1 hydrochloric acid or nitric acid carefully, with stirring, to the hot solution to neutralize excess alkali and decompose carbonate. A precipitate of silica will probably appear. After a point the mixture will start getting brownish. Stop adding acid, and filter. Add to the hot filtrate about 25 grams of strontium chloride hydrate and enough concentrated ammonia (about 4 ml) to cause the formation of a large yellow precipitate of strontium chromate. Cool to room temperature and filter off this precipitate. It may be possible to recover more strontium chromate from the filtrate by adding ammonia. Wash the precipitate with dilute ammonia water, dry it, and weigh.

To prepare potassium dichromate from this strontium chro-

[24] See H. A. Doerner, *Chem. and Met. Eng.*, **47** (1940), 688.

mate, add the calculated amount of potassium acid sulfate dissolved in about 50 ml of water, and digest on the steam bath until the solid appears pure white. This process should take about half an hour. Then filter and evaporate the filtrate until crystals start to form. Cool to near 0°, filter off the crystals, dry, and weigh. Calculate the percentage yield, assuming that the chromite contained 30 per cent of chromium.

QUESTIONS

1. Give two other examples of preparations involving oxidation in a fused alkali.

2. About what pH is reached when acid is added to the solution of the melt until carbon dioxide is just given off?

3. Suppose a great excess of acid were added to the solution of the melt; what would happen to the chromate? (Remember that the melt originally contained potassium nitrate.)

4. Why are strontium ions, rather than barium ions, chosen to precipitate the chromate?

5. What are the practical difficulties in performing small-scale fractional crystallizations?

6. How would you prepare potassium chromate from potassium dichromate?

36. Ammonium Molybdate and Molybdenum Oxide from Molybdenite

In performing this experiment, remember that molybdenum is just below chromium in the periodic table, and watch for similarities and differences between molybdenum and chromium.

Molybdenite, molybdenum sulfide, can be converted to the oxide by roasting in air. Heat 10 grams of molybdenite, finely powdered, in an iron dish over a Meker burner or a ring burner. You will probably notice immediately that the ore particles have a thin film of oil on them; in writing your report, explain how this got there. Heat to a dull red heat (not higher) for about 30 minutes, stirring with a spatula to allow free contact with air. When no more gray particles are seen and the mass is yellow, allow to cool. Note any color change on cooling. The product is mainly molybdenum trioxide.

Transfer the oxide to a beaker, add 30 ml of water and 10 ml of concentrated ammonia, and warm on the steam bath for about

15 minutes, stirring frequently. Filter. The residue is mainly iron oxide. Evaporate the filtrate on the steam bath until crystals form, then cool to near 0° and filter. Dry and weigh the ammonium molybdate crystals.

Molybdenum trioxide. Grind the ammonium molybdate to a fine powder and heat in a small evaporating dish supported on a fire-clay triangle, stirring occasionally, until no more ammonia is given off. Various color changes will be observed; observe and interpret them. The residue is nearly pure molybdenum trioxide discolored by small traces of a lower oxide. It could be obtained quite pure by heating in oxygen. Weigh and compare the yield with the theoretical.

QUESTIONS

1. The solution of ammonium molybdate is usually light blue in color, yet the crystals are white. Explain.

2. What is the usual effect of heat on the color of a substance? Give three or four examples to illustrate this effect and offer a theoretical explanation.

3. How is molybdenum metal obtained from the oxide? Can chromium metal be obtained in this way?

4. How is molybdenum metal made and fabricated commercially? What are some of its uses?

5. What is the effect of heat on ammonium dichromate? Account for the difference from the effect of heat on ammonium molybdate.

6. Compare the properties of molybdenum trioxide and chromium trioxide.

37. Selenium Dioxide: Selenious and Selenic Acids[25]

Selenium dioxide. Selenium can be oxidized to the dioxide by burning in air, or by the action of concentrated nitric acid. The latter is the better by far, since it is more complete, faster, and easier to control.

Place 50 ml of concentrated nitric acid in an evaporating dish *in the hood,* and warm on a wire gauze or sand bath to about 40 to 50°. Then add 20 grams of powdered selenium, a little at a time, scattering it over the surface of the acid. The reaction is quite vigorous, and it is a good idea to place a large inverted funnel over the dish to catch the spray. Red-brown fumes of nitrogen

[25] *Inorganic Syntheses,* 1, 119. *Systematic Inorganic Chemistry,* Chapter 10.

dioxide are evolved. This is poisonous, and so are all selenium compounds; so do this experiment in a good draft. When all the selenium has been added, evaporate the solution cautiously just to dryness. Cool, add a few milliliters of fresh concentrated nitric acid (or, better, fuming nitric acid), and again evaporate just to dryness. This evaporation may be done on the steam bath.

Grind up the product, place it in an evaporating dish, and moisten with a very little concentrated or fuming nitric acid. Place a dry inverted funnel over the dish, and heat the dish over a flame. Selenium dioxide sublimes at 317° in long needles that should be perfectly white, any pink color being due to unoxidized selenium. The yield should be nearly quantitative, when allowance is made for the percentage purity of the selenium used as starting material.

Selenic acid. Use one of the two following procedures:

1. Dissolve 15 grams of selenium dioxide in 50 ml of 30 per cent hydrogen peroxide, and let the solution stand overnight. Then reflux for 12 hours in an all-glass apparatus, adding a few milliliters more hydrogen peroxide toward the end. The resulting solution of selenic acid is about 2 molar.[26]

2. Dissolve 10 grams of selenium dioxide in 150 ml of water and stir thoroughly while adding a solution of 32 grams of silver nitrate in 120 ml of water. When the precipitate has settled, pour off the mother liquor and nearly neutralize it with concentrated sodium carbonate solution. A further quantity of the fairly soluble silver selenite is obtained. Wash this precipitate once by decantation and add it to the main quantity of the precipitate.

Wash the combined precipitate once by decantation and then with ice water on the Büchner funnel until the washings give no test for silver. If it is necessary to leave the silver selenite at this point, cover it with water; do not let it dry out.

Suspend the washed silver selenite in 500 ml of water and stir thoroughly with a mechanical stirrer having a glass paddle. Add slowly the theoretical amount of bromine for the reaction

$$Ag_2SeO_3 + Br_2 + H_2O \rightarrow H_2SeO_4 + 2AgBr$$

Then add a slight excess of bromine and allow to stand for 2 hours. The solution should still have an orange color at the end. Filter

[26] L. I. Gilbertson and G. B. King, *J. Am. Chem. Soc.*, **58** (1936), 180.

off the silver bromide on a glass filter cloth or asbestos mat, and draw air through the filtrate at room temperature to remove the excess bromine.

The resulting solution should be about 0.2 molar and can be used for the subsequent tests. It contains a little hydrobromic acid, which can be removed by the cautious addition of dilute silver nitrate if a very pure product is desired.[27]

Tests of solutions of selenious and selenic acids

Perform the following tests with approximately 0.1-molar solutions of each acid. If selenic acid was made by procedure (1) above, the sample of solution used for the tests should be boiled for an hour to decompose any hydrogen peroxide.

1. Test with litmus.

2. Pass sulfur dioxide gas into about 10 ml of each solution.

3. Test with solutions of potassium bromide and potassium iodide. (If no reaction occurs right away, warm for a few minutes before concluding that there is no reaction.)

4. Test with barium chloride solution and dilute hydrochloric acid.

5. Selenic acid is said to be the only acid which in pure aqueous solution will attack gold. Perform experiments to see if it will attack gold leaf.

The ionization constants of selenious acid. If a pH meter or electrometric titration apparatus is available, titrate a suitable volume of 0.1 molar selenious acid with 0.2 molar sodium hydroxide, and plot a graph of pH against volume of sodium hydroxide, paying particular attention to the regions near the two end points, where 1 mole and 2 moles of sodium hydroxide have been added for each mole of selenious acid. The second end point will be sharper than the first, and the first end point can best be located by dividing by 2 the volume of sodium hydroxide needed to reach the second end point.

Read off the pH for the volume of base halfway between the first and second end point. At this point the concentrations of $HSeO_3^-$ and $SeO_3^=$ are very nearly equal, and

$$[H^+] \approx k_2 \frac{[HSeO_3^-]}{[SeO_3^=]} = k_2, \text{ the second ionization constant.}$$

[27] L. M. Dennis and J. P. Koller, *J. Am. Chem. Soc.*, **41** (1919), 949.

Now read off the pH at the first end point. At this point

$$[H^+] = \sqrt{k_1 k_2}$$

To prove this equation, remember that we have here a solution of $NaHSeO_3$ and that $[H_2SeO_3]$ and $[SeO_3^=]$ are very nearly equal.

Compare your values with the values $k_1 = 2.4 \times 10^{-3}$ and $k_2 = 4.8 \times 10^{-9}(25°)$ obtained by Hagisawa.[28]

Isomorphous selenates and sulfates. Many sulfates and selenates are isomorphous and very similar in appearance. It might be of interest to prepare small samples of $CuSeO_4 \cdot 5H_2O$ and $Na_2SeO_4 \cdot 10H_2O$ and compare them with the corresponding sulfates. The formation of mixed crystals by sodium sulfate and selenate could be investigated by using the analytical method for selenium described by Dennis and Koller.[29]

Selenium dioxide as an oxidizer in organic chemistry. Selenium dioxide is a specific agent for oxidizing activated methylene groups to :CO groups.[30]

QUESTIONS

1. Which is the stronger acid, (a) H_2SeO_3 or H_2SeO_4, (b) H_2SeO_3 or H_2SO_3? On what general rules do you base your answers?

2. How does the oxidizing power of the elements in their higher oxidation states depend on the atomic weight in B subgroups of the periodic table, e.g., Ge, Sn, Pb, or As, Sb, Bi, or Se, Te?

3. Of the acids H_2SeO_3 and H_2SeO_4, which is the more powerful oxidizing agent? Which is the more rapidly acting oxidizing agent?

4. Compare the physical properties of the elements sulfur and selenium.

38. Potassium Permanganate

Potassium permanganate is obtained from manganese dioxide by oxidation in two stages. The first is carried out by fusion with alkali (potassium hydroxide) in the presence of air or another oxidizing agent and yields potassium manganate, K_2MnO_4. This is taken up in water and decomposed into potas-

---

[28] *Bull. Inst. Phys. Chem. Res. (Tokyo)*, **18** (1939), 648.

[29] *J. Amer. Chem. Soc.*, **41** (1919), 949.

[30] Reviews of the use of selenium dioxide in organic oxidations are written by R. P. Linstead, *Annual Reports of the Chemical Society*, 1937, page 238, and G. W. Watkins and C. W. Clarke, *Chemical Reviews*, **36** (1945), 235.

sium permanganate and manganese dioxide by carbonic acid, a weak acid.

In an iron sand bath place 40 grams of potassium hydroxide and 15 grams of potassium chlorate. Air would perform the necessary oxidation, but potassium chlorate is faster. Heat over the flame of a Fisher burner until the mixture is just melted but is not too hot. Add, a little at a time, 25 grams of manganese dioxide, stirring with the end of a file. As manganese dioxide is added, the iron dish is heated hotter to keep the contents soft, until finally, when all the manganese dioxide has been added, the dish is heated with the full heat of the burner. Keep at this temperature for 15 minutes; then cool and extract the mass with 500 ml of boiling water. (This step may be done conveniently by placing the iron dish in water in a large evaporating dish and boiling.) Filter the solution through a plug of glass wool. Note its color.

Place the solution in a large beaker and boil. At the same time pass in carbon dioxide until the liquid is purple with no trace of green. (Small pieces of dry ice may be stirred in, instead of passing carbon dioxide gas.) The color is very deep and is best seen by putting a drop of solution on a piece of filter paper. The stain must show no trace of green. Stop heating at this point. Stand to allow the sediment to settle. Decant the supernatant liquid into an evaporating dish and evaporate down to 150 ml. Filter hot through a small glass-wool plug (best under suction) and allow the filtrate to cool, cooling finally in ice. Collect the permanganate crystals on a glass-wool or asbestos filter. Dry in the air and weigh.

Note: After the fused mass is extracted with water, the experiment must not be interrupted but must be completed the same day.

The best way to remove manganese dioxide stains is by means of a weakly acidified 3 per cent solution of hydrogen peroxide.

For an alternative, and possibly cleaner way of producing potassium manganate from manganese dioxide, see Experiment 52, Part B.

QUESTIONS

1. Several other compounds containing metals in high oxidation states, besides potassium manganate, can be made by fusing a lower oxide with alkali and at the same time exposing to air. Name two such compounds and write equations for the reactions involved.

2. How would you produce (a) potassium manganate, (b) manganese dioxide, from potassium permanganate?

3. Why is potassium permanganate not satisfactory as a primary standard in volumetric analysis?

39. Potassium Iodate

Iodine can be oxidized to iodate by potassium chlorate. The iodine simply replaces the chlorine in the chlorate, giving potassium iodate and chlorine. This substitution is possible because iodine has a smaller electron affinity than chlorine. The reaction goes best in acid solution, possibly because of the intermediate formation of a little chloric acid.

Dissolve 30 grams of potassium chlorate in 60 ml of warm water in a 250-ml flask. Add 35 grams of iodine to the solution, then 1 ml of concentrated nitric acid. Heat until the reaction begins. Chlorine is given off rapidly and the flask must be kept under the draft. The reaction is exothermic. As long as it is going rapidly, no external heat is necessary, but when it slows down, heat until all the iodine has reacted and most of the chlorine has been boiled off. Then add another gram (no more) of coarsely powdered iodine to make up for loss of iodine by vaporization during the reaction and continue boiling until all the chlorine and excess iodine have been driven off. Evaporate the solution until crystallization starts; then cool thoroughly and pour off the mother liquor.

Dissolve the crude salt in 150 ml of hot water. Besides KIO_3 it contains some of the acid salt, $KH(IO_3)_2$. A solution of 5 grams of potassium hydroxide in 50 ml of water is therefore added slowly until the solution is neutral to litmus. On cooling, pure potassium iodate crystallizes. The solubility is 10 grams per 100 ml of water at 25° and 4.7 grams per 100 ml at 0°, so that an increased yield can be obtained by evaporating further or by cooling in ice before filtering. However, a yield of 80 per cent can easily be obtained. Dry the salt in air.

Determination of purity. Weigh accurately about a gram of your product and dissolve it in water in a 100-ml volumetric flask and make up to the mark, shaking well. Be sure that all the salt has dissolved, since it dissolves slowly in cold water. Pipette out 10-ml portions and run them into 50 ml of water to which you have added 1 ml of 6N sulfuric acid and about 2 grams of potassium iodide. Titrate the liberated iodine with the standard thiosulfate provided, adding starch indicator when the iodine color is nearly gone. Write equations for the reactions in this titration and calculate the percentage purity of your potassium iodate.

Qualitative tests

1. *The "clock reaction."* Sulfurous acid reduces iodate to iodine in a sequence of three consecutive reactions. First, iodate is reduced to iodide. Second, iodide, iodate, and hydrogen ion react to form iodine. Third, iodine oxidizes more sulfurous acid to sulfuric. The first stage is the slowest, the last the fastest. Consequently, no iodine appears until the sulfurous acid is all used up.

A solution is provided which is 0.01M in Na_2SO_3 and 0.04M in sulfuric acid and which also contains starch. (This solution must be freshly made.) Put 25 ml of this solution in a flask and add 25 ml of 1 per cent potassium iodate, mixing quickly. After a few seconds the whole solution suddenly turns blue or black because of the liberation of iodine. The appearance of the iodine can be delayed by using more dilute solutions or by using less iodate. This reaction, performed in more concentrated solution, is used to make iodine from the iodate in Chile saltpeter (see Experiment 46). Write equations for the consecutive reactions involved.

2. Heat a very little potassium chlorate (about 10 mg) with concentrated sulfuric acid in a dry test tube. Then repeat, using potassium iodate instead of chlorate. Write equations for the probable reactions and explain the difference in behavior in the light of the general relations between the halogens.

QUESTIONS

1. In the reaction between potassium chlorate and iodine, which gains electrons, iodine or chlorine? Is the direction of electron transfer any different from that occurring when chlorine reacts with potassium iodide to displace iodine?

2. Which is the more powerful oxidizing agent, iodic or chloric acid?

3. In this preparation, acid potassium iodate was an undesired by-product that had to be neutralized with alkali. Is there an acid potassium chlorate? Explain.

40. Cuprous Salts

(A) *Cuprous chloride.* In this preparation cupric copper is reduced to cuprous by reaction with metallic copper. Dissolve 43 grams of cupric chloride crystals ($CuCl_2 \cdot 2H_2O$) in 100 ml of water in an Erlenmeyer flask, add 100 ml of concentrated hydrochloric acid and 25 grams of fine copper turnings. Heat over a low flame, keeping the air out of the flask by a small watch glass laid over the mouth of the flask, until no further color change is observed and the solution is pale straw colored. The solution now contains cuprous copper in the form of a soluble complex, probably H_2CuCl_3. Pour the solution into a 2-liter bottle containing 1500 ml of tap water which has been shaken with 50 ml of ether. (The ether drives out some of the dissolved air.) CuCl separates as a fine white powder, which is filtered off and washed with water to which a few drops of dilute hydrochloric acid have been added, then with two successive 30-ml portions of alcohol, then with 30 to 50 ml of ether. The wash liquids must be distributed evenly over the whole precipitate and must not be sucked through too fast. As one wash liquid disappears into the cake of precipitate, the next wash liquid is added. The precipitate must not be sucked dry until after the ether washing. The product should be white; if it turns green on standing because of oxidation, it is because it has not been properly dried. The yield is nearly theoretical.

(B) $Cu(NH_3)_2Cl$. Place a gram or two of cuprous chloride in each of two dry test tubes. Fill the tubes completely with ammonia water (1 part concentrated ammonia to 2 of distilled water) and immediately close with rubber stoppers. Shake until all the solid is dissolved and note the color of the solution. Then empty out about two-thirds of the contents of one of the tubes and shake the remainder of the solution with the air in the tube. Compare the color of the solution that has been shaken with air with the color of the solution that has not. Explain the change, writing a balanced equation for the reaction between air and ammoniacal cuprous chloride solution.

(C) *Cuprous iodide.* To a few milliliters of a dilute (0.05M) cupric sulfate or chloride solution add some solid crystals of potassium iodide and shake until these are dissolved. Note what has happened and explain, writing the equation.

Note: Instead of 43 grams of cupric chloride crystals, the equivalent amount (80 grams) of potassium cupric chloride from Experiment 4 may be used to make the cuprous chloride.

QUESTIONS

1. What is the function of the alcohol and of the ether in the washing?

2. Suppose the cuprous complex with hydrochloric acid had been $H^+ \cdot CuCl_2^-$. Would it have yielded cuprous chloride when poured into water?

3. Why does potassium iodide give cuprous iodide, whereas potassium chloride does not give cuprous chloride, when added to a cupric sulfate solution?

41. Silver Nitrate from Silver Residues

This method of silver recovery can be applied to any silver precipitates from quantitative analysis, such as silver chloride, bromide, or thiocyanate. First wash the residues well with water by decantation and on the Büchner funnel, then spread out on paper to dry. A little nitrobenzene absorbed on the precipitate from the Volhard titration will not do any harm; the greater part of the nitrobenzene will be removed by washing, in any case.

Take 50 grams of dry residues, 100 grams of anhydrous sodium carbonate, 75 grams of potassium carbonate, and 25 grams of sodium or potassium nitrate. Grind them up together and mix well. Pack the mixture into a large Hessian fire-clay crucible, tamp down with a pestle, and fill the crucible right up to the top, putting in more mixture if necessary. Heat the crucible in a Fletcher gas furnace for 3 or 4 hours. A little caution is needed here, because the alkali carbonates in the crucible will attack the silicates of the crucible walls and may make a hole in the side of the crucible if the heat is too intense. The crucible should therefore be placed on the side of the furnace away from the hole where the flame comes in, the maximum heat possible with a full gas supply should not be used, and the bottom of the furnace should be covered over with sand beforehand to lessen the damage to the furnace if a leak should occur.   Ordinarily, however, the crucible will not fail.

At the end of the fusion, the mass in the crucible should be quiet, with no bubbling.   When the crucible is cool enough to handle, break it open with a hammer and take out the silver button.   Hammer away as much as possible of the adherent slag and flatten the button out somewhat, and weigh it.

Wash the button with a little 6M hydrochloric acid and water, then put it into a beaker with 75 ml of concentrated nitric acid and 50 ml of water; heat it on the steam bath, or, better, on a hot plate in the hood until all the silver has dissolved.   Filter the solution if necessary.   Evaporate on the steam bath or hot plate to about 75 ml; cool slowly, finally cooling in ice.   Filter the crystals of silver nitrate on a Büchner funnel, preferably one with a sintered glass plate, suck as dry as possible, and spread the crystals out on a watch glass to dry.   The solubility of silver nitrate is high, even at 0° (122 grams salt to 100 grams water), so it may be worth while to evaporate down the mother liquor further and obtain a second crop of crystals, which, however, will not be as pure as the first.   The first crop, if dried well enough to remove adhering nitric acid, will normally be pure enough for most purposes.   It can, of course, be recrystallized if desired.   The purity of the salt should be checked by analysis, especially if the salt is to be used in the analytical laboratory.

Silver nitrate stains the fingers.   Clean hands the day after this experiment are a sign of excellent technique.

QUESTIONS

1. Write equations for the reactions undergone by AgCl in this process, including all likely intermediates.

2. Why are both sodium and potassium carbonates used in the fusion?

3. What will be the effect of excess of nitric acid on the solubility of silver nitrate?

4. Suppose the silver residues contained salts of lead and copper; would these contaminate the silver nitrate?   Explain your answer.

42. Barium Chloride from Barytes

Barytes (barium sulfate mineral) is reduced with carbon at a red heat to barium sulfide, which is treated with hydrochloric acid to produce barium chloride. The mineral contains a little iron as an impurity; this is removed before the barium chloride is crystallized out. The reduction with carbon takes 2 hours, so you should start as soon as possible and do other work during the heating period.

Start up the Fletcher gas furnace first. The air and gas must not be turned on fully until the furnace is warmed up, or the burner may go out. While the furnace is heating, weigh out 24 grams of powdered barytes (or barium sulfate, technical grade) and 6 grams of finely powdered charcoal, mix, and rub the mixture a little at a time in a mortar to give more intimate mixing. Good mixing is important. Transfer to a small Hessian fire-clay crucible and tap the powder down; then spread charcoal on top of the mass to form a covering layer. Put a cover on the crucible (a small evaporating dish, concave side up, will do), and heat to full redness for 1 hour. At the end of this time pull the burner away from the furnace and then turn it off. Do *not* turn it off while it is still placed against the furnace aperture, or the heat of the furnace will melt the gauze of the burner. (For a description of the Fletcher furnace and its operation, see Chapter II.)

When the furnace has cooled sufficiently, take out the crucible, keeping it covered. When it is really cool, empty out the contents on a sheet of paper. In a small beaker place 40 ml of water and 20 ml of dilute (6M) hydrochloric acid; then stir in the powder from the crucible, a little at a time, *in the hood*, until there is no effervescence. Test with litmus; if alkaline, add a little more acid. Add powder and hydrochloric acid alternately, testing with litmus when necessary until all the powder has been added and the solution is as nearly neutral as possible (slightly acid rather than slightly basic). About 30 ml of 6M acid will be used.

The iron in the mineral is now in the ferrous condition. Oxidize it to ferric by boiling the solution until it no longer smells of hydrogen sulfide, and then adding a few drops of bromine water and boiling a little longer. Now add, with stirring, a little precipitated barium carbonate, until all the iron is thrown out of solution. Not more than a gram of barium carbonate should be needed. Filter; then evaporate the filtrate, which should be clear and colorless, down to about 40 ml or until crystals appear. Cool; then collect and dry the crystals of $BaCl_2 \cdot 2H_2O$. The yield is about 60 per cent, based on the assumption that the mineral was pure $BaSO_4$. The amount of barium chloride left in the mother liquor can be estimated from the solubility, 35.5 grams $BaCl_2$ to 100 grams of water at 20°.

QUESTIONS

1. Name two other sulfides commonly obtained from the sulfates in this way.

2. What is the chief use for barium sulfide?

3. Why is the iron oxidized to ferric before being precipitated with barium carbonate?

4. Suppose no stock of pure barium carbonate is available; how would you proceed to get a product which is free from iron?

43. Lead from Lead Monoxide

This experiment illustrates two of the reactions that occur during the production of lead from lead sulfide ore. The ore is first roasted to convert some or all of the sufide to lead monoxide. The monoxide can be reduced to lead by either reducing it with carbon or simply by heating it in the absence of air with more lead sulfide.

(A) Mix 15 grams of lead monoxide (litharge) with 1 gram of carbon black, grinding the two together a little at a time in a mortar, then mixing on a piece of paper until you have a uniform grayish powder. Place in a small iron crucible. Cover the crucible (a porcelain cover will do) and heat to redness with a good Meker or Fisher burner for half an hour or more. Then allow to cool somewhat, and while the crucible is still faintly red-hot pour the contents into cold water in an iron dish. Wash away the excess of carbon carefully and collect the lead, which is in the form of small globules with a good deal of carbon adhering to it. To make these cohere, melt some anhydrous borax in your iron crucible and add the powder of lead and carbon a little at a time; then heat to redness for a few minutes with a cover on the crucible to keep in the heat. Pour the molten mass out into an empty iron dish supported on asbestos, or onto a sheet of asbestos paper. Chip the borax glass away from the lead and weigh the latter.

(B) Mix intimately as before 22 grams (0.10 mole) of lead monoxide with 12 grams of finely powdered galena (lead sulfide mineral), and place the mixture in a small fire-clay crucible. Set this in a Fletcher furnace which has been started previously and is now red-hot. Since melted litharge attacks fire-clay and just possibly might make a hole in the crucible, it is a good idea to cover the bottom of the furnace with sand before you start. Cover the crucible, and heat at full redness for half an hour to an hour. Remove the crucible from the furnace. When it has cooled somewhat, pour the contents into an empty iron dish supported on asbestos. Alternatively, let the crucible cool completely and break it open with a hammer. Separate the lead from the slag and weigh.

The second reaction cannot be performed in an iron crucible, because iron reacts rapidly with lead sulfide at a red heat to form iron sulfide and lead.

QUESTIONS

1. How is it that the oxides of most metals, such as lead, zinc, iron, and tin, can be reduced easily with carbon, even though the oxide and carbon are both solids and come in contact only at a few points?

2. Write equations for all the reactions in the smelting of lead sulfide. Note that lead sulfate is sometimes one of the intermediate products. Include reactions with carbon, but do not include reactions of impurities in the ore.

3. What is the slag formed in Part B?

44. Hydroxylamine Hydrochloride

Hydroxylamine salts are made commercially in two ways: the hydrolysis of primary nitroparaffins[31] and the cathodic reduction of nitric acid. In the laboratory it is easiest to reduce nitrous acid with a bisulfite and then hydrolyze the resulting salt of hydroxylamine disulfonic acid. The reactions are as follows:

$$HONO + 2HSO_3^- \rightarrow HO \cdot N(SO_3)_2^- + H_2O$$
$$HO \cdot N(SO_3)_2^- + 2H_2O \rightarrow HO \cdot NH_3^+ + 2SO_4^- + H^+$$

In the first stage of the process it is important to keep the solu-

[31] See Lippincott and Hass, *Ind. Eng. Chem.*, **31** (1939), 118.

tion cold (below 0°) and to keep it neutral (above pH 6). The procedure which follows is that of Rollefson and Oldershaw.[32]

Dissolve 0.5 mole (42.5 grams) of potassium nitrite and 0.6 mole (58 grams) of potassium acetate in 200 ml of water in a 2-liter flask, and cool in an ice-salt freezing mixture to about −5°. Add 750 grams of finely crushed ice, shaking frequently. (A mechanical stirrer is not satisfactory.) Pass sulfur dioxide slowly. A mass of crystals of potassium hydroxylamine disulfonate, $HO \cdot N(SO_3K)_2 \cdot 2H_2O$, crystallizes out. When the odor of sulfur dioxide shows that an excess has been passed, filter off these crystals under suction and wash them with 100 ml of ice water. The yield is about 85 per cent.

The solution should remain almost colorless while passing the sulfur dioxide, and some ice should be left at the end. If the temperature rises too high, a yellow solution containing salts of $N(SO_3H)_3$ results.

Heat the potassium hydroxylamine disulfonate with 500 ml 0.5M hydrochloric acid on the steam bath for 2 or 3 hours, or boil gently for this time. Add 0.45 mole of solid barium chloride (111 grams of the hydrate) to the hot solution, stirring well until it has all reacted or dissolved, then filter off the precipitated barium sulfate, washing the filter cake with a little hot water. Evaporate the filtrate and washings to dryness. During evaporation, cubical crystals of potassium chloride separate; these may be filtered off and discarded. Grind up the dry residue in a mortar and boil it for a few minutes with about 200 ml of 95 per cent alcohol. (Absolute alcohol is better but is not essential.) On cooling, the filtrate deposits hydroxylamine hydrochloride, $NH_3OH^+ \cdot Cl^-$, in fine needles, containing not more than a few tenths of 1 per cent of potassium chloride as an impurity. More hydrochloride can be obtained by evaporation of the solution. The yield from the disulfonate should be quantitative.

One part of hydroxylamine hydrochloride dissolves in 4 parts of 95 per cent alcohol by weight at the boiling point, and in about 12 parts at 25°.

Tests

1. To a solution of hydroxylamine hydrochloride add bromine water. From your observations write a probable equation for the reaction.

[32] *J. Am. Chem. Soc.*, **54** (1932), 977.

2. Test an acidified solution of hydroxylamine hydrochloride with an aqueous solution of mercuric chloride, and also with a solution of titanous chloride if available. Write equations for the reactions.

3. Test an aqueous solution of hydroxylamine hydrochloride with litmus.

QUESTIONS

1. What was the purpose of the potassium acetate in this preparation?

2. How does hydroxylamine compare as a base with ammonia? Is it a strong or a weak base?

3. How is free hydroxylamine, NH_2OH, prepared?

4. What is the reaction of hydroxylamine with nitrous acid?

45. The Transition Elements; Chromous Acetate

(A) *Oxidation states of transition elements.* In four large test tubes place about 20 ml of dilute solutions of titanic chloride, ammonium metavanadate, potassium dichromate, and ammonium molybdate. Add to each about 10 ml of concentrated hydrochloric acid and several grams of granulated or mossy zinc. Set under the draft. Note all the color changes and interpret them by means of ionic equations.

(B) *Preparation of chromous acetate.* Set up the apparatus shown in Fig. 24. A Büchner flask is fitted with a two-hole stopper through which passes a dropping funnel and a tube that reaches right to the bottom of the flask. The side tube of the Büchner flask is connected by a short piece of rubber tubing with a tube which dips under water to absorb hydrochloric acid fumes. In the flask put 10 grams of powdered potassium dichromate and 50 grams of mossy zinc. Meanwhile prepare a solution of 90 grams of sodium acetate hydrate in 80 ml of water. If this had to be heated to make the sodium acetate dissolve it must be cooled before use. Add through the dropping funnel dilute hydrochloric acid made by mixing 150 ml of concentrated acid with 75 ml of water. (You probably will not need all the hydrochloric acid.) A vigorous reaction takes place. Add acid to keep the reaction going until the liquid in the flask has become a pure blue in color. The chromium is now all in the chromous condition. While the hydrogen is still being rapidly evolved, pinch the rubber connection on the side tube with the fingers, forcing the solution in the flask out of the other tube and into the sodium acetate solution that is contained in a 300-ml Erlenmeyer flask. Chromous acetate separates in this flask as a brick-red precipitate. Stopper the flask immediately to prevent access of air, and cool under the tap.

The precipitate must now be washed and dried. This is the most difficult part of the experiment. Good washing with water is necessary to remove sodium acetate and other associated salts;

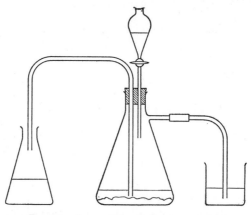

Fig. 24.   Preparation of chromous acetate.

yet the precipitate is appreciably soluble in water and, moreover, oxidizes very quickly while wet.

Filter the chromous acetate on a Büchner funnel and wash with four 50-ml portions of ice-cold air-free water. (Water may be freed from dissolved air by bubbling nitrogen or by shaking with a little ether as in Experiment 40). Pour one portion on as soon as the other has drained and see that the wash water is distributed over the whole precipitate. Then wash with 75 ml of alcohol and 75 ml of ether and suck dry. Spread the precipitate on a piece of paper to let all the ether evaporate; then weigh the yield. It should be about 75 per cent of theoretical and should be a light brick-red powder.

Washing and drying chromous acetate is an excellent test of technique. If done well, the product should remain red indefinitely in a dry, tightly closed screw-cap bottle; otherwise the material goes green by oxidation very soon. A good way of keeping the product from oxidizing during washing and drying is to cover the Büchner funnel with a loosely fitting cork stopper carrying an inlet tube through which passes carbon dioxide, removing it only when necessary to add wash liquid. A 6-cm coarse-grade sintered-glass filter funnel, Büchner shape, is ideal for this filtration.

QUESTIONS

1. Could (a) iron, (b) tin be substituted for zinc as the reducing agent in the chromous acetate preparation? Give reasons for your answer, referring to a table of standard electrode potentials (Table 6, page 48).

2. How could you prepare a pure specimen of chromous chloride? What would be the chief difficulty in this preparation?

3. How might vanadium tetrachloride, VCl_4, be prepared? What physical and chemical properties might it be expected to have?

46. Iodine from Potassium Iodate

Much iodine is obtained from Chile saltpeter, which contains a small amount of iodate. The iodate remains in solution after the sodium nitrate has been crystallized out and is reduced to iodine by treatment with sodium bisulfite. Exactly the correct amount of bisulfite must be added; if too much is added, some iodine is reduced to the iodide ion, whereas if too little is added, unreacted iodate remains.

Dissolve 0.15 mole of iodate (32 grams of KIO_3 or 30 grams of $NaIO_3$) in 300 ml of water. Also dissolve about 45 grams of sodium bisulfite in 300 ml of water. The purity of the sodium bisulfite cannot be taken for granted, so that it is necessary to find experimentally the volume of bisulfite solution which is needed to react with the iodate. This volume is determined as follows: Fill a burette with your iodate solution. Pipette 10 ml of bisulfite solution into an Erlenmeyer flask and add 20 ml of water and a few drops of starch solution; then add the iodate solution from the burette until a permanent blue color results. Add the iodate slowly as the end point is approached. You have now added 3 moles of bisulfite to 1 of iodate, according to the reaction

$$3HSO_3^- + IO_3^- \rightarrow I^- + 3SO_4^= + 3H^+$$

Note the volume of iodate solution added and return the rest of the iodate from the burette to your stock. Measure the volume of your iodate solution and calculate the volume of your bisulfite solution that must be added to it to bring about the reaction

$$5HSO_3^- + 2IO_3^- \rightarrow I_2 + 5SO_4^= + 3H^+ + H_2O$$

Note that there is no need to throw away the solution in your titration flask. The amounts already mixed here can be counted in with the rest.

Mix the iodate with the required volume of bisulfite in a 1-liter flask; stopper after mixing and cool thoroughly (heat is developed in the reaction). Prepare a filter consisting of a thin layer of asbestos supported on a small glass-wool plug in the neck of a glass filter funnel. Filter the precipitated iodine under suction on this filter. The filtrate should be a light brownish color. Suck the iodine as dry as possible on the filter. Then transfer it to a porcelain dish. (A steel spatula should not be used to handle iodine.) Dry it as follows: Pour on it about 10 ml of concentrated sulfuric acid. Cover the dish with a watch glass and heat cautiously over a small flame until the iodine melts under the acid. Cool. Pour off the sulfuric acid; then rinse the solid cake of iodine with water and dry with filter paper.

The product is now purified by sublimation. Place the dried iodine in a dry 9-cm evaporating dish and over it place an Erlenmeyer flask half full of cold water. The outer surface of this must be dry. Heat the dish with a small flame for 15 to 30 minutes until all the iodine has sublimed and condensed on the under surface of the flask. Scrape it on to a piece of paper and transfer quickly to a glass-stoppered weighing bottle. Note the yield.

QUESTIONS

1. What would the filtrate, after mixing the iodate and bisulfite, look like if you had added (a) too much bisulfite, (b) too much iodate? How would you make sure you had mixed these substances in the right proportion?

2. What impurities might commercial iodine contain that would *not* be removed by sublimation?

47. Manganese and Chromium by the Goldschmidt Reaction

In the Goldschmidt reaction, mentioned in Chapter VI, a metal oxide is reduced by aluminum powder to the free metal. The reaction is useful for obtaining transition metals, such as vanadium, chromium, and manganese, which are too reactive to be produced by reduction of their oxides with hydrogen. The reaction

$$\text{metal oxide} + \text{Al} \rightarrow \text{metal} + \text{Al}_2\text{O}_3$$

is highly exothermic, and both the metal and the aluminum oxide are melted by the intense heat. For this reason the reaction is used to produce small quantities of molten iron for welding purposes (thermit welding). Some judgment is necessary to control the vigor of the reaction. If it is too vigorous, material is blown out of the crucible or is lost by vaporization; if it is not vigorous enough, the charge does not all react, or else the alumina does not melt and the metal remains dispersed as small globules instead of collecting in one mass. The intensity of the reaction can be controlled to some extent by choosing the particle size of the aluminum and the degree of oxidation of the metal oxide used. Both methods are used in the procedures following. The quantities given below are suitable for a 150-ml Hessian fire-clay crucible.

(A) *Manganese.* First prepare a quantity of brown manganomanganic oxide, Mn_3O_4, by heating 200 grams of powdered manganese dioxide, or pyrolusite, to bright redness for an hour. Mix 60 grams of the cooled Mn_3O_4 with 20 grams of fine aluminum turnings, such as one would get from the laboratory shop, and pack the mixture into the bottom of a 150-ml Hessian crucible. Press it around the sides so that a depression is left in the middle. Fill this depression and the rest of the crucible with a mixture of 100 grams of Mn_3O_4 and 33 grams of 30-mesh aluminum powder. The finely powdered aluminum used for paint must *not* be used, since it reacts too violently. Even the 30-mesh powder is too reactive to be used for the whole charge; this is why the aluminum turnings are used.

Press a hole about 1 cm across and 4 to 5 cm deep into the top of the charge, and fill it with a mixture of 15 grams of barium peroxide and 2 grams of magnesium powder. It is well to dig a little of this mixture into the main charge at the bottom of the hole with the point of a spatula. Pack the crucible around with sand in a small bucket or large can. Finally insert a piece of magnesium ribbon into the barium peroxide-magnesium ignition powder to serve as a fuse. About 4 in. of ribbon should be exposed. Light the end of the magnesium ribbon and retreat a few yards. When the charge is ignited, showers of sparks are thrown about three feet into the air, so it is best to perform the experiment out of doors. Otherwise take precautions to see that the sparks do no damage.

The contents of the crucible should settle down cleanly to a white-hot mass in the bottom. Further quantities of the mixture of oxide and 30-mesh aluminum may be added to the white-hot crucible if a larger yield of manganese is desired. The operator should wear goggles and a heavy glove and use a long-handled iron spoon to add the reaction mixture. However, it is not necessary to add more of the mixture, since a fair yield of manganese is obtained with the one charge as described.

When the crucible has cooled completely, break it open and crack the mass with a hammer. The manganese comes out cleanly in the form of a button, which, however, is rather brittle. The yield from a single charge is only about 60 per cent, mainly on account of loss of manganese by evaporation.

(B) *Chromium.* The reduction of green chromic oxide, Cr_2O_3, by aluminum does not furnish sufficient heat in a small crucible to melt the alumina completely. The green oxide is therefore mixed with one-third its weight of chromium trioxide, CrO_3. The latter is hygroscopic, but mixing it with the very fine Cr_2O_3 powder protects it from atmospheric moisture to some extent.

Weigh out 100 grams of green chromic oxide and place it in a large dry beaker; then quickly weigh out 33 grams of chromium trioxide and mix it with the green oxide. Then add the theoretical amount (62 grams) of 30-mesh aluminum powder and mix well. Pack the mass into a 150-ml Hessian crucible, press a hole in the top of the charge as in the preparation of manganese, and pack the hole with a mixture of 15 grams of barium peroxide and magnesium powder. Embed the crucible in sand, insert 5 in. of magnesium ribbon into the barium peroxide-magnesium mixture, and fire as in Part A above, taking the same precautions. The reaction is very vigorous and gives a smooth white-hot melt.

When the crucible is cold, crack it open with a hammer and remove the button of chromium. The yield is nearly quantitative. The chromium may be used to prepare anhydrous chromic chloride, from which certain complexes of chromium can be made; the manganese may be used in the electrolytic preparation of potassium permanganate (see Experiment 52).

Tests

1. Compare the hardness and type of fracture of chromium and manganese.
2. Treat small slivers of each metal with hot water, dilute sulfuric acid, and dilute sodium hydroxide solution.

QUESTIONS

1. The *Handbook of Chemistry* lists the following heats of formation per mole at 18°C. The negative sign states that heat energy is lost on formation, that is, that the reactions (metal + oxygen) are exothermic. Calculate ΔH, the heat absorbed, at 18° for each of the three reactions performed in this experiment. What information would you need to have to calculate the heats of reaction for the actual conditions of this experiment?

Heats of formation: Al_2O_3 -380 kcal/mole Cr_2O_3 -273 kcal/mole
Mn_3O_4 -345 kcal/mole CrO_3 -139 kcal/mole

2. The heat of formation of MgO is -146 kcal/mole at 18°C. Calculate the heat of reaction of Mg with Cr_2O_3. You will note that it is considerably greater than the heat of reaction of Al with Cr_2O_3. Why, then, do we not use magnesium instead of aluminum to carry out the more difficult Goldschmidt reductions?

3. What nonmetals are advantageously prepared by the Goldschmidt reaction?

48. Potassium Peroxydisulfate

The salts of peroxyacids can be prepared by adding hydrogen peroxide to a normal oxyacid salt, as sodium peroxyborate was in Experiment 27. Another common method of preparation is by electrolytic oxidation. Anodic oxidation is very similar in its effects to the action of hydrogen peroxide. Some workers believe that hydrogen peroxide is actually formed at the anode as an intermediate in electrolytic oxidation.

Potassium peroxydisulfate, $K_2S_2O_8$, also known commonly as potassium persulfate, is one of the easiest salts to prepare by electrolytic oxidation, because it is only slightly soluble and separates from solution in good yield. The electrolyte is a solution of potassium acid sulfate, $KHSO_4$, saturated at about 5°, that is, containing about 40 grams of salt to 100 grams of water. The anode is a short piece of platinum wire, 1 cm of 22 gauge (0.644 mm diameter) being satisfactory, and the cathode is a small strip of platinum foil. The cathode should be placed an inch or two above the anode. Reduction of persulfate at the cathode is inappreciable, and it is not necessary to separate anode and cathode by a porous pot. Good yields of persulfate are obtained by using a high current density and a low temperature. Addition of a little fluoride raises the yield somewhat.

Take about 150 ml of potassium acid sulphate in, preferably, a tall narrow "electrolytic" beaker, and surround the beaker by an ice bath. Add about 0.1 gram of sodium fluoride if desired, though it is not necessary. Insert the electrodes, and pass a current of 1 to 1.5 amp for 2 hours. Six volts will be sufficient potential and will not require a rheostat, since the current can be adjusted by moving the cathode up and down. Keep a record of the time and the current, and maintain the current constant to 0.1 amp, so that you can calculate the number of coulombs passed and thence the theoretical maximum yield for the reaction $2HSO_4^- \rightarrow S_2O_8^- + 2H^+ + 2e$.

Potassium peroxidisulfate separates as a crystalline precipitate after the first 10 minutes. At the end of the electrolysis, filter the precipitate on a small sintered glass filter or a Gooch crucible, wash with alcohol and ether, and dry. The yield is about 5 grams. From the yield, calculate the *current efficiency*, that is, the observed yield divided by the maximum theoretical yield for the quantity of electricity passed. The current efficiency should be about 50 per cent.

The peroxydisulfate can be produced faster by passing a higher current, with a longer wire for the anode, if the solution is kept cold—a condition that can be maintained only with very efficient stirring.

Tests

1. Test an aqueous solution of potassium peroxydisulfate with acidified potassium iodide solution and with titanic sulfate solu-

tion (Experiment 28). Compare the reactions with those of hydrogen peroxide.

2. Prepare a solution of peroxymonosulfuric acid, H_2SO_5, by mixing a little ice-cold concentrated sulfuric acid with potassium peroxydisulfate, keeping the mixture ice-cold for a minute, and then diluting with water. Repeat, with this solution, the tests given above.

3. To 5 ml of dilute (M/10) chromic sulfate solution add a little dilute sulfuric acid and two drops of M/10 silver nitrate; then stir in about half a gram of potassium peroxydisulfate. Warm the solution to about 50° and leave for 10 or 15 minutes.

4. Repeat Test 3, using manganous sulfate instead of chromic sulfate.

5. To a little silver nitrate solution in a test tube add dilute nitric acid and about a gram of potassium peroxydisulfate. Dissolve as much of the peroxydisulfate as you can, then add 2 or 3 ml of pyridine. A complex salt of dipositive silver is produced.

QUESTIONS

1. Write structural formulas for peroxymono- and peroxydisulfuric acids, and show how these formulas explain the differences in reaction you found in Tests 1 and 2 above.

2. Write equations for the reactions you observed in Tests 3 and 4.

3. Can peroxydisulfuric acid or its salts be prepared by starting with hydrogen peroxide and without using an electric current? If so, explain how.

4. Indicate briefly the use of potassium or ammonium persulfate in quantitative analysis.

5. What is the action of silver nitrate in the oxidations observed in Tests 3 and 4?

49. Potassium Chlorate

When a solution of sodium or potassium chloride is electrolyzed, chlorine is formed at the anode and hydrogen and the alkali hydroxide are produced at the cathode. In alkali-chlorine cells, such as the Nelson cell, the cathode and anode products are kept from mixing by a diaphragm. If the diaphragm is omitted and if the cell is designed so as to give the best possible mixing of the chlorine from the anode with the alkali from the cathode, hypochlorite or chlorate is formed by the reactions

$$Cl_2 + 2OH^- \rightarrow Cl^- + OCl^- \tag{1}$$
$$3OCl^- \rightarrow 2Cl^- + ClO_3^- \tag{2}$$

The second reaction is favored by heat and acidity. In cold, slightly alkaline solutions, hypochlorite is the main product; in warm, weakly acid solutions, chlorate is formed almost exclusively. The chloride that results as a by-product in these reactions is reoxidized at the anode. By electrolysis of a concentrated sodium chloride solution at 30 to 60° and pH 6.7, some 85 per cent of the chloride can be converted into sodium chlorate. The chlorate and unreacted chloride are separated by first evaporating at 100°, which precipitates most of the sodium chloride, then cooling to 20° to crystallize the chlorate.[33]

The efficiency of the electrolytic oxidation is limited to some extent by the reduction of chlorate at the cathode. To check this reduction as far as possible, a little chromate or dichromate is added to the bath. This is partially reduced at the cathode to tripositive chromium, which forms a coating of a chromic chromate around the cathode and thus inhibits the cathodic reduction of chlorate or hypochlorite.

In this experiment, potassium chlorate will be prepared, since it is much less soluble than sodium chlorate and less soluble than potassium chloride; this property makes it easier to separate than sodium chlorate. The electrolytic cell is shown in Fig. 25. The cathode is a steel tube with holes drilled in the sides at the surface of the solution; the anode, concentric with it and reaching not quite to the bottom of the cathode tube, is a rod of compressed graphite. The graphite electrodes used in spectrographic analysis are satisfactory; they disintegrate a little in use, but not much. Arc carbons are not satisfactory, since they disintegrate a great deal. The electrode assembly is mounted in a large test tube, which can be placed in a bath of hot water. This arrangement provides good circulation of solution and good mixing of the chlorine and potassium hydroxide.

The electrolyte is a solution of 100 grams of potassium chloride and 1 gram of potassium dichromate in 300 ml of water. (The cell shown has a capacity of about 90 ml.) The potassium

[33] P. H. Groggins, A. L. Pitman, and F. H. Davis, *Chem. and Met.*, **45** (1938), 692, and **47** (1940), 468.

dichromate supplies the slight acidity needed for the chlorate production, as well as inhibiting the cathodic reduction.

Heat the cell to about 45°, and electrolyze at 2½ to 3 amperes for 8 hours. Since there is a slight loss of chlorine, with accompanying increase of alkalinity, add 1 ml of 1N hydrochloric acid every 2 hours. To prevent any possible attack of the steel cathode, the current should be kept flowing the whole time and not turned off. Keep a record of the current flowing and the time. Toward

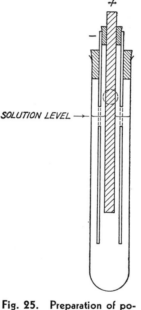

SOLUTION LEVEL →

Fig. 25. Preparation of potassium chlorate.

the end of the run, potassium chlorate crystals will separate, along with fragments of graphite from the anode. At the end, remove the electrodes, turn off the current, and cool the solution in the cell to 0°. Filter the crystals of chlorate and suck as dry as possible; then dissolve them in a minimum of hot water, filter from suspended graphite, and let the solution cool slowly to 0°. Filter and dry the crystals, which should be pure white flakes. Test their purity by dissolving a little in water and adding silver nitrate; there should not be more than a faint cloudiness.

From your yield and the quantity of electricity passed,

calculate the current efficiency. Allow as far as possible for the chlorate left in solution during the crystallizations. The solubility of potassium chlorate at 0° is 3.3 grams per 100 grams of water and will be depressed by the excess of potassium chloride present.

QUESTIONS

1. It is good for the solution to be slightly acid but definitely harmful for it to be too strongly acid. What happens when a strong acid is added to a solution containing a chloride and a chlorate?

2. The potassium dichromate serves somewhat to control the pH. Explain how.

3. What bearing has the use of dichromate or chromate in chlorate cells on their properties as corrosion inhibitors?

4. Outline some of the important uses of chlorates.

5. What are chlorites, and how are they made from chlorates?

50. Potassium Perchlorate

Perchlorates are made commercially by the electrolytic oxidation of chlorates. Sodium perchlorate is made first as a rule, and other perchlorates are prepared from it by double decomposition. The conditions for a good yield of perchlorate[34] are concentrated neutral chlorate solution, temperature below 50°, current density 0.1 amp/cm² or more, and anode of platinum. Platinum is better than graphite, probably because of its higher oxygen overvoltage.

A Slomin electroanalyzer is very convenient for making perchlorates in the laboratory. This apparatus plugs into ordinary a-c sockets and delivers about six volts across each pair of electrodes. Voltmeters and ammeters are built into the instruments, as are rheostats for controlling the current. With the models generally in use, two electrolyses can be run at a time. The cylindrical platinum-gauze electrodes supplied for electroanalysis are suitable for the perchlorate preparation, and the inner gauze cylinder can be rotated while the current is passing, thus giving good stirring.

Dissolve 50 grams of sodium chlorate in 100 ml of water, and add 0.05 gram of potassium chromate and 0.05 gram of potassium

[34] S. Glasstone and A. Hickling, *Electrolytic Oxidation and Reduction.* London: Chapman & Hall, 1935, pages 376–378.

dichromate. Insert the gauze cylinder electrodes about halfway into the solution, and turn on the current to its maximum value (over 1 amp), making the inner electrode the anode, that is, with the NORMAL-REVERSE switch pointing to NORMAL. Turn on the motor so that the anode rotates, and leave running for 4 or 5 hours. Note the current from time to time, and note also the time for which it passes. The electrolysis can be interrupted and resumed later if desired. The temperature of the solution will rise to 40° or 50°. The area of the gauze anode described is about 40 square centimeters in all, or 20 square centimeters when half immersed. The effective area is about half this, since the inner surfaces probably do not carry much of the current. In the author's experiments, the gauze anode had an over-all diameter of 14 mm and a length of 50 mm.

When the electrolysis is finished, calculate the number of coulombs passed and the theoretical maximum yield of perchlorate in moles. Measure out an equal number of moles of potassium choride, in the form of a saturated (4M) solution, and stir this into the warm electrolyte. A fine perchlorate precipitate appears. Cool in ice and filter the potassium perchlorate on a small Büchner funnel. Wash with a little ice-cold water and suck as dry as possible; then dissolve the crude product (which contains some chlorate) in 150 ml of hot water and recrystallize, cooling to below 10° before filtering off the crystals. Wash the crystals with about 50 ml of ice-cold 50 per cent alcohol, suck dry, and dry in air. The yield of recrystallized salt, based on the current consumption, is about 60 per cent.

The recrystallized salt is tested for chlorate as follows: Dissolve about 0.1 gram in 5 ml of warm water in a large test tube, add an equal volume of cold saturated sulfur dioxide solution, and boil the solution immediately to drive off sulfur dioxide. As soon as there is no more smell of sulfur dioxide, cool and add a little dilute nitric acid and silver nitrate. There should not be more than a slight turbidity. Chlorate is rapidly reduced to chloride by sulfurous acid under these conditions, whereas perchlorate is hardly reduced at all.

If a Slomin analyzer is not available, any arrangement with a platinum anode which gives a current density of 0.05 amp/cm² or more can be used. The cathode may be of steel. Keeping the solution cool improves the yield. It would be very interesting to make a number of runs with different temperatures and current densities (preferably with the Slomin analyzer, because of the good stirring it gives) to study the effect of these factors.

QUESTIONS

1. Compare the appearance or "crystal habit" of potassium perchlorate and potassium chlorate.

2. Why is sodium chlorate more suitable than potassium chlorate as the electrolyte?

3. Why are both chromate and dichromate added to the electrolyte?

4. Name two important uses for perchlorates.

5. How would you distinguish potassium perchlorate from potassium peroxydisulfate (Experiment 48)? How do these compounds differ in structure?

51. Titanous Chloride Solution

This experiment will illustrate the general technique of electrolytic reductions. A cell with a diaphragm is used, since the titanous chloride would be reoxidized if it were allowed to come into contact with the anode or anode products. The cathode is of lead, since lead has a high hydrogen overvoltage. The cathode chamber is enclosed, since titanous chloride is slowly oxidized by air. The same general method can be used to reduce other metals to salts of low oxidation states. For example, it can be used to prepare salts of $+3$ or $+2$ vanadium or of $+2$ chromium. However, a much more elaborate technique must be used in handling solutions of dipositive chromium or vanadium, since these are oxidized immediately upon contact with air.[35]

The apparatus is shown in Fig. 26. The electrolysis cell is a tall 250-ml beaker without spout, a so-called "electrolytic beaker," and it is closed with a large rubber stopper. The anode chamber is a small porous cup of test-tube form. This must have sufficient porosity to conduct the current but not so much that the anode solution can diffuse out freely. The author tried an alundum Soxhlet thimble and found it unsatisfactory. A piece of the "candle" used in bacterial filters should be satisfactory. The author has used a sintered glass Gooch crucible, medium

[35] Directions for preparing solid chromous sulfate electrolytically are given by A. Asmanow, *Z. anorg. Chem.*, **160** (1929), 210.

porosity, with the lower apron sawed off, as shown in the diagram. The anode in this experiment is a graphite rod. The cathode is a strip of thin sheet lead, about 5 × 12 cm, with an extension 1 cm wide that is folded upward and passes between the rubber stopper and the wall of the beaker. It is best to prepare this lead cathode by making it anodic in 2N sulfuric acid for a short time, then reversing the current until the lead dioxide formed anodically has all been reduced to metallic lead. A very thin film of finely divided lead results and makes the electrode more efficient as a

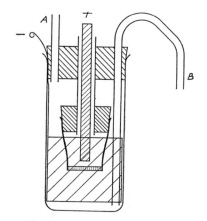

Fig. 26.   Preparation of titanous chloride solution.

cathode for electrolytic reduction. Alternatively, the lead may be prepared by amalgamation, by sandpapering and then rubbing with a wad of cotton moistened with mercuric chloride solution. Perhaps this method of preparation is better than the first for this particular experiment.

Prepare a solution of titanium tetrachloride as follows: Place 35 ml of concentrated hydrochloric acid in a 250-ml Erlenmeyer flask and cool in ice; pour in, a little at a time and with shaking, 25 grams (14.5 ml) of pure titanium tetrachloride; then add, slowly and with shaking, 75 ml of water. The solution should be colorless and almost, if not quite, clear. Commercial titanium tetrachloride contains iron and should not be used. It is best to use the product from Experiment 18, made from pure titanium dioxide. Use appropriate precautions in handling this very corrosive fuming liquid.

Put the titanium tetrachloride solution into the electrolytic beaker, pour 4M hydrochloric acid into the anode chamber, assemble the cell, and immediately start electrolyzing. (It is best to start the electrolysis before lunch and finish it in the afternoon.) Pass a current of 1 amp and set the cell in a large beaker of cold water to keep the temperature down. Reduction proceeds at the cathode with almost 100 per cent current efficiency. Calculate the minimum time required for complete reduction to $TiCl_3$. Shortly after this time has elapsed, bubbles of hydrogen will be seen forming at the cathode. Continue the electrolysis for about half an hour longer, then shut off the current and immediately transfer the solution to a 125-ml Erlenmeyer flask by blowing illuminating gas down tube A and holding the flask under tube B. Immediately close the flask with a rubber stopper; then dismantle the electrolysis cell.

The titanous chloride solution should be just over 1 molar. Its strength may be checked by pipetting out 2 ml, delivering this from the pipette under the surface of 50 ml of acidified M/20 ferric sulfate solution, shaking, and titrating the ferrous ion with N/10 permanganate or ceric sulfate. If an M/10 solution of titanous chloride is required, the solution from the electrolytic cell can be transferred to a bottle containing 900 to 1000 ml of freshly boiled distilled water. For analytical purposes the solution must be stored in a bottle fitted with a burette so arranged that the solution does not come into contact with air, either during storage or while the burette is being filled. Such devices are described in textbooks of volumetric analysis. The 1M titanous chloride keeps very well in an ordinary stoppered flask, and the flask may be opened several times without appreciable oxidation.

If crystalline $TiCl_3 \cdot 6H_2O$ is desired, it can be obtained by evaporating the 1M solution in a vacuum desiccator.

Tests

1. Add a little titanous chloride solution to a dilute solution of copper sulfate.

2. To 10 ml of M/5 titanous chloride add 3 per cent hydrogen peroxide, drop by drop, until there is no further change.

3. To the solution from the previous test add a little concentrated potassium fluoride solution.

4. To a solution of methylene blue of about 0.1 per cent concentration add a few drops of titanous chloride solution. Then pour in M/20 ferric sulfate, 1 ml at a time, while shaking. Note the use of methylene blue as an indicator in titanous chloride titrations.

QUESTIONS

1. In Experiment 45 a solution of titanous chloride was made by reducing titanic chloride with zinc and hydrochloric acid. What advantage does the electrolytic method have over this procedure?

2. Could a platinum cathode be used instead of lead?

3. Why may amalgamated lead be better than pure lead for the cathode in this preparation?

4. Show, by numerical calculations from oxidation-reduction potentials and solubility products, that the result of Test 1 was to be expected.

52. Potassium Permanganate, Electrolytically

Permanganates can be made by electrolytic oxidation in two ways. In one method an anode of manganese or a manganese alloy is used, with potassium carbonate solution as the electrolyte; in the second method a potassium or sodium manganate solution, obtained by alkaline oxidation of manganese dioxide, is oxidized to permanganate at an iron anode. The second method is the one usually used commercially. Both methods are illustrated in this experiment.

(A) *From manganese.*[36] A porous pot is used to separate the anode and cathode solutions; use a small pot, about 2 × 10 cm, and set it in a 250-ml beaker. Prepare an approximately 6N potassium carbonate solution by diluting saturated potassium carbonate solution with one-half its volume of water, and pour exactly 150 ml of this solution into the beaker; then pour more of the same solution into the porous pot so that the levels inside and outside the porous pot are the same. Use as cathode a strip of iron or a spiral of thick iron wire suspended inside the porous pot. For the anode use a strip of ferro-manganese (85 per cent Mn) or, better, the lump of manganese obtained in Experiment 47; suspend this by means of a battery clip so that it is half immersed in the solution. Do not let the battery clip dip into the solution. Arrange a glass tube so that air may be bubbled through the

[36] G. Grube and H. Metzger, *Z. Elekt.*, **29** (1923), 100.

solution in the beaker to keep it stirred. Pass about three bubbles a second and let the air bubble over the surface of the anode. Set the cell in a trough through which cold water circulates. The lower the temperature, the better the yield of permanganate; keep the temperature of the electrolyte below 25° if possible.

For best results the current density at the anode should be about 0.15 amp/cm², but it will probably be necessary to exceed this value to complete the experiment in a reasonable time. Pass a current of 3 to 4 amp for at least 4 hours. During the first 2 hours, take out 2.0-ml samples every 20 minutes, run them into an excess of 6N sulfuric acid, and titrate the permanganate with 0.1N ferrous ammonium sulfate solution. Calculate the permanganate concentration, and plot on a graph the number of equivalents of permanganate produced against the number of faradays of electricity passed, and also the current efficiency. This will be less than 30 per cent.

After 2 hours or less, solid potassium permanganate should start to crystallize out. This effect will be manifest by an apparent sharp drop in the current efficiency as found by titration. After 2 hours, shut off the current temporarily, remove the anode and clean it (it will be found to be coated with manganese dioxide), and restore the alkalinity of the solution by adding 1 mole of solid potassium hydroxide for each faraday of electricity passed. If this is not done, potassium bicarbonate will crystallize along with the permanganate.

Continue the electrolysis for at least 2 hours more, then filter the solid permanganate crystals on sintered glass or asbestos, and recrystallize if desired. The yield is very small—only a few grams—partly on account of the low current efficiency and also because it takes 7 faradays of electricity to produce a mole of permanganate, so that the process would be slow at the best. Probably for this reason the process has not found wide commercial application.

(B) *From potassium manganate.*[37] The potassium manganate is prepared from pyrolusite as follows: Dissolve 30 grams of potassium hydroxide in its own weight of water in a shallow iron

---

[37] K. Brand and J. E. Ramsbottom, *J. Prakt. Chem.*, **82** (1910), 336. See also E. R. Riegel, *Industrial Chemistry*, 4th ed. New York: Reinhold, 1942, page 316.

dish, add 20 grams of finely powdered pyrolusite, and heat over a flame, evaporating to dryness while stirring constantly with the end of a file. When the mass is quite dry, heat to moderate redness for two hours, using a muffle furnace if necessary. Stir the mass at intervals to allow free access of air. The potassium hydroxide and manganese dioxide react with oxygen to form potassium manganate, K_2MnO_4. Let the mass cool, grind it to a powder, and add it to 300 ml of hot water in a flask. Stopper the flask and shake vigorously for some minutes, then set aside to settle. Siphon off as much as possible of the supernatant liquid and filter it through glass wool.

A similar procedure was used to make potassium manganate in Experiment 38. There potassium chlorate was used to help the oxidation. Potassium chlorate cannot be used in this experiment, because the resulting chloride would attack the anode during electrolysis.

The electrolytic oxidation is performed in a two-compartment cell like that in Part A, but using a larger beaker. The anode solution may either be in the beaker or in the porous pot. The anode is preferably of nickel gauze, but a spiral of thick iron wire is also satisfactory. The cathode is a small spiral of thick iron wire. The cathode solution is 1M potassium hydroxide, the anode solution the potassium manganate solution prepared above. The anode solution should be kept stirred during the electrolysis, either by a stream of filtered air or by a mechanical stirrer. The temperature is 30° or below. The lower the current density at the anode, the better the yield, but a current density of 0.1 amp/ cm^2 is satisfactory. Pass a current of about 2 amp.

Measure the volume of the manganate solution before adding it to the cell, and titrate a 1-ml portion by adding it to 20 ml of 0.1N ferrous ammonium sulfate plus 2 ml of 6N sulfuric acid and back-titrating the excess of ferrous salt with 0.1N potassium permanganate. As the electrolysis proceeds, withdraw 1-ml portions after 15, 30, 45, and 60 minutes and titrate in the same way. After about an hour, potassium permanganate should start to crystallize out. The oxidation of manganate to permanganate should be complete after 3 hours at 2 amps. Set the anode solution aside in a cool place, and when crystallization is complete, filter the crystals on asbestos or sintered glass and suck them dry.

From the results of the titrations, calculate the proportion of the manganese dioxide that was converted to manganate in the first operation, and calculate the current efficiency for permanganate production for each 15-minute period during the electrolysis. The current efficiency should be nearly 100 per cent at the beginning of the electrolysis.

QUESTIONS

1. The solubility of potassium permanganate in water at 20° is 6.4 grams per 100 grams of water. From the solubility product relation calculate the approximate solubility in 6N potassium carbonate.

2. List as many factors as you can that limit the over-all efficiency of Process B, and suggest ways of making this process more efficient.

3. Give equations for two nonelectrolytic methods of converting potassium manganate to permanganate.

Index

Page numbers in **heavy type** refer to the preparation of the substance listed.